2 Steps Behind!

2 Steps Behind!

113 poems and illustrations
dedicated to the preservation of our wild animals
by
Dawn Lawrence

Foreword by Virginia McKenna
Founder of the Born Free Foundation

Published by Aldabra Publishing
'Five Wishes', Jarvis Close, Stalbridge, Dorset DT10 2PQ

Text Dawn Lawrence 2013
Illustrations Dawn Lawrence 2013

First published 2013
by Aldabra Publishing
'Five Wishes', Stalbridge, Dorset DT10 2PQ

Printed in Great Britain by
Acanthus Press 01823 663339

ISBN 978-0-9575988-0-5

Foreword

In my wildest dreams I never imagined I would actually smile when I read the word 'extinction'. Nor find a Gharial endearing. But when I read this delightful and engaging collection of poems, I did just that.

This kind of approach to the possibility that some of the world's species may become extinct is, in itself, quite rare. It is not written by an erudite scientist, overloading us with fearsome facts and figures. It is actually 'written' by the animals themselves! They tell us where they live, how they live, what they like, what they eat and what they fear. One of these fears is that before very long they will have vanished from the earth. Then they will survive only as a poem, a picture or a dream.

I challenge you not to be charmed by the brilliant Blue Poison Dart Frog, or the strange little Pyrenean Desman — two of the extraordinary creatures of whom, I admit, I was totally ignorant. Oh, and I mustn't forget the Spotted Cuscus, or the Tuatara (known as a living fossil).

Increasingly alarm bells ring for rhino, tiger, elephant and lion. But this fascinating, informative and endearing collection of animal 'autobiographies' (surely for children <u>and</u> grownups) will carry you into a whole new, and often invisible, world. It will, I believe, make the hardest of hearts care about all kinds of creatures and, surely it will make all of us, young and old, determined to protect them. Never mind if we can't see them. They deserve to live for their own sake, filling their own particular space and fulfilling their own particular purpose on our fragile little earth.

Virginia McKenna

Virginia McKenna
Born Free Foundation

Acknowledgements

The author wishes to express her gratitude to Virginia McKenna, British stage and screen actress, author and wildlife campaigner and Founder of the Born Free Foundation, for the several valuable amendments she drew attention to, and for her encouragement and help in supporting this project.

She also wishes to remember her good friend, Jenny Jones, for her editorial guidance over the years, and a great many thanks are due to her husband Clyde, without whose inexhaustible patience and good humour this book would never have been possible.

2 Steps Behind!

Dragons and dinosaurs,
Both are consigned
To a legendary world
Now left far behind;
And those creatures today
Have but one thing in mind;
'Can't you see,' they exclaim,
'We're just two steps behind!

'The planet is bursting,
With life *billions* strong,
Yet there's little space left
Where *we* might belong;
And new species are lost
In a long endless list,
Before people have learned
That we even exist.

'But we breathe the same air,
We're related to *you,*
And you might – if you act –
Save the last of the few.
The dinosaur's fate
Should bring us to mind,
We're following closely
Just two steps behind!'

Contents

Contents

THE AARDVARK

You might not have heard of an Aardvark,
My name means both *earth* and a *pig*;
And you'll guess how the two are related
When I tell you that Aardvarks can dig.
At night-time we hunt ants and termites,
Those that live in a large earthen mound;
But during hot African sunlight,
We hide in a hole underground.

I'm pig-like because of my body,
With long head and long narrow snout,
No creature on Earth is quite like me,
You'll agree if we meet, without doubt.
I've webbed feet with ears like a rabbit,
I've sharp digging claws like a bear;
My kangaroo tail will surprise you,
And I'm covered with bristly hair.

Yet an Aardvark is shy and defenceless,
I'm the only one left of my kind;
Guess who are my closest relations?
There's not very many, you'll find.
There's manatee; elephant; hyrax;
Three names that won't enter your head,
(But *pig* must *never* be mentioned)
We aardvarks are very well bred.

I know there are those who admire me,
I'm a bandit; I'm daring; I'm brave;
I break into nests under darkness,
It's quite reckless the way I behave.
I attack ants - most fierce and ferocious -
Those soldiers most war-like to see;
Fifty thousand I'll eat at one sitting,
I need truckloads to satisfy *me.*

I know that you'll say, 'Just one moment,
Don't ant-eaters do just the same?'
And I have to agree we share the same tastes,
And we look quite alike, that is plain;
But an ant-eater isn't related,
I'm a creature that's out on my own;
A solitary, strange looking mammal,
With body parts all quite unknown.

My tongue is long, narrow, and snake-like,
I've shovel shaped nails on each toe;
And these things make an aardvark look ugly,
He's weird looking, wrinkly, and slow.

But **Aardvark** of course begins with an *A*,
A lesson that everyone's missed;
It's really quite clever to add one more letter,
With an *A* - I'll be top of your list!

THE WANDERING ALBATROSS

'Please tell me all about yourself,
You lovely wandering bird,
For I shake my head in disbelief
At all the things I've heard.'

'I'm called the Wandering Albatross
From the South Atlantic sea;
But there are many species
With different names to me.
I'm the largest sea bird in the world,
With wings the greatest length;
Wings that keep me borne on air,
Which give me speed and strength.
I'm marked with black and wavy lines,
You cannot see in flight,
So viewed from any distance
I'm always coloured white.
And if you were to follow me,
You'd cross the world's great seas,
To perish in a blazing sun,
Or on an ice-cap freeze.'

'But tell me, lovely Albatross,
The place you call your home;
And if you fly with other birds,
Or if you fly alone.'

'I roam the Southern oceans,
There's nowhere I call home;
I'll often spend six months at sea,
But always fly alone.
Each year I reach Australia,
And stay some months until
I change my route to Uruguay,
And the seas around Brazil.
Man tracks me now by satellite,
And studies me for days,
But still he cannot fathom out
My history or my ways.
Who else would scour the very globe
To bring food to their young?
It seems the puzzles that I pose
Have only just begun.'

'But won't you tell me, Albatross,
What you do when you reach land?
For a life that's spent upon the wing
Is hard to understand.'

'Those islands in the Southern seas
Are there to serve my need,
And on their grassy levels
I'll rest, and there I'll breed.'

'But then, do tell me, Albatross,
Can the tale be true?
That with your chosen life-long mate,
There's a famous dance you do?'

'It's a lengthy, noisy, complex dance,
Bill fencing is the aim;
But we also bow and prance around,
And make it quite a game.
We've been apart for weeks, you see,
And I mean *weeks* and *weeks;*
So colonies all come alive
With the loud 'clap' of our beaks.
We make a sort of singing sound,
As we swing from side to side;
Or we face each-other standing tall,
With both bills open wide.'

I thanked my friend, the Albatross,
For his interesting news;
And then I had some of my own,
But not the sort I'd choose.

'I know from what I'm told about,
And then by reading books,
That each year thousands of you die,
All drowned by fishing hooks.
And when you've spent six months or more
(That's half a year) at sea,
And travelled all the seas on earth,
That's life's worst tragedy.'

'It could easily be avoided,'
The Albatross then said,
'But vessels tow long baited lines,
And kill us birds instead.
We try to eat the bait of course,
And are dragged beneath the sea;
So to stop this needless slaughter
Each captain must agree
In view of sea birds everywhere,
To change his way of fishing,
And tens of thousands will be saved
Instead of only *wishing*.
We circle earth a dozen times,
And every ocean cross;
How long in moments would it take
To save *one* Albatross?'

And moved to tears I answered him,
'You make the world seem small,
No creature can compare with you;
I love **you** *most of all.'*

THE GIANT ANT-EATER

They call me Giant Ant-Eater,
But it's confusing I agree,
When you think of other Ant-Eaters
Who seem a lot like me.

There's my friend the Giant Pangolin
Who lives across the sea,
But he has scales and I have not;
One difference you will see.
He looks rather like a pinecone
When he rolls into a ball,
Whilst *I* just sleep beneath my tail,
I'm not like *him* at all.

My tail is quite delightful,
It's really heaven sent;
And when I curl up for a sleep,
I use it like a tent.

It's a handy good umbrella
In every kind of weather,
And covers me completely,
Like a giant ostrich feather.

I live in South America,
With those who look like me;
And though we all have fur the same,
The others climb a tree.
The Amazon is where I swim,
It's quite a treat for me
To wade about on swampy land,
But I'll never climb a *tree.*
I live completely on the ground,
And though others share my name,
Remember I'm the giant one,
Of great Ant-Eater fame.
To give you some idea of size -
I'm a full two metres long,
With bushy tail and fearsome claws,
And, like a bear, I'm strong.

I'm famous for my sticky tongue
Of most astounding length,
And then, of course, as I've just said,
I've also awesome strength.
My sense of smell soon finds my prey -
A tempting termites' nest;
And once my claws have dug them out,
My tongue will do the rest.
I'm quite the ants' worst nightmare

With my long ferocious tongue;
But I have to scrunch them quickly,
As I sometimes *do* get stung!
Then I'll shuffle through the forest,
All on my lonely own,
Or out upon the grasslands,
For there's nowhere I call 'home'.

Each cub of mine till one year old,
Will travel with its mother;
And she will teach what they must learn,
And pass to one another.
Whilst each clings tightly to her fur,
And rides upon her back,
They listen to her good advice
In case of an attack:

"To show you mean no nonsense,
Stand high on your hind feet;
You will quickly strike with terror
Those few enemies you meet.
Then use your claws like daggers -
The ones with which you dig -
For don't forget how sharp they are,
How frightening and big!
Those claws of yours are lethal,
And so is each great paw;
And all who come within their reach,
Shall quickly breathe no more!"

THE PRONGHORN ANTELOPE

No other creature in the world
Will take your breath away
Like me. Just listen carefully
To what I have to say:

Throughout the world there's just one place
To find the likes of me,
And that is North America,
Where I'm still running free.
I live upon the mighty plains,
The prairies of the West;
And once you hear what *I* can do,
You'll quite forget the rest.

So ancient is the Pronghorn breed,
That I'm the living link
With Ice Age animals on earth
All mostly now extinct.

Of every mammal listed,
It still is little known
How pronghorns are unique for speed,
And almost stand alone.
Only the cheetah, famed for this,
Can travel quite so fast;
But over greater distances,
Even *he* can't last.

For a longer more enduring course,
There's no creature known on earth
That runs – and keeps on running
From the moment of its birth.
I'll stretch to *sixty* miles an hour,
And that's a modest score;
Whilst fawns can reach to *forty-five*,
Which might surprise you more.

Even when a few hours old,
A Pronghorn runs with speed;
It's no wonder everyone declares
'A most amazing breed.'

No other creature in the world
Is related close to me;
My name-sake is my hallmark,
My horns that you can see.
I'm the only creature living,
That yearly sheds a horn;
Deer and elk have antlers,
But mine with prongs are worn.

I'm tough as well as super fast,
It's amazing when you think
I'll thrive upon a thorny plant,
Last days without a drink,
Eat cactus no-one else will eat,
Survive the bitter cold;
And desert heat will suit me well,
I've known them all of old.

I have a clever trick I play,
To tell when danger's near;
I flash the white hairs on my rump
To make my warning clear;
But I'm easily recognisable,
I'm such a striking sight,
With the gold upon my body,
And my head and neck marked white.

A man once said - the story goes -
When first he viewed our herds:
"They come and go in the flash of an eye,
As swift as a flight of birds".
That was when the world was young,
When our herds were millions strong;
But the spirit that moved the heart of man
Is still here where I belong!

THE ARMADILLO

When children see me passing by,
they cry *'Whatever's that?*
A funny little armoured tank - no bigger than a cat!'
I'm rather like a crocodile, with eyes just like a pig,
With donkey's ears, a rat's long tail,
and little claws that dig.
I'm rather like a tortoise – but a tortoise I am not -
I look just like an alien, a creature Time forgot.

That's what they say about me,
and what they say is right,
I really am astonishing; I'm quite the strangest sight.
I've special armour plating with lots of horny scales,
Which is excellent protection, it hardly ever fails.
My tongue is long and sticky;
think how useful when I dine;
It catches *ants* - my favourite food –
four thousand at a time!
I can dig a hole like lightning,
That's something else I do;
In less than half a minute
I'll have disappeared from view.

It's true some armadillos curl,
and roll into a ball,
But *everyone* can't do this trick –
and certainly not *all.*
We spend our days just sleeping.
You might say 'lazy lot!'
But since we work while others sleep,
we simply say, *Why not?*
There's something you might read in books
(which happens to be true)
No creature living on the land
can do what armadillos do:
They'll hold their breath *six minutes long.*
A record, I declare!
It's handy when we cross a pond
and need that extra air.
If we sink down to the bottom,
we can hold on till we stand,
Or else we'll fill ourselves with air
and float until we land.

There's *giant* armadillos, and a *fairy* that is pink;
They have to call us different names to sort us out I think.
But when you come across us, whatever kind you choose,
An Armadillo's special and will *always* make the news.
Remember how we hold our breath?
That's brilliant you'll agree,
It's got the experts scratching heads
as how we came to be!

Find me in North, Central, and South America

THE AYE-AYE

You pronounce my name as *'eye-eye'*,
It's as simple as can be;
And I live in Madagasgar,
Should you wish to visit me.

The sounds I make are very small,
I might just say *'Hi! Hi!'*
But say it quickly and you'll find
It sounds a lot like *Aye-Aye.*

I'm the largest primate in the world
That's active just at night,
A science fiction character
Who looks the strangest sight.
My big ears are like satellites -
Those that can track a star -
Supersensitive to sound,
Though I cannot hear *that* far.

But I *can* tune in to tiny grubs
Hidden deep within a tree,
And I'll tap with one long finger,
Then poke to get them free.

The middle finger of my hand
Is bony and so long
It looks just like a skeleton's,
Where you'd think it should belong;
But every finger on each hand
Is creepy, long and thin;
You'd think I was the Devil's child,
A creature born of sin.

My two front teeth - like Dracula's -
Just seem to grow and grow;
And then at night I jump through trees,
Or on four feet I'll go,
And creeping from my tree-top nest
Where I have slept all day,
I'll sneak off very quietly
To hunt and feed, or play.

I'm not afraid of human beings,
I'll stroll down any street;
But sad to say most villagers
Don't find me very sweet;
They think that I'm enchanted
Like a spooky witch's cat;
And I'm often cursed or even *killed*.
(They believe in things like that.)

Though birds live on my island,
No woodpeckers live here,
So I'm the nearest thing to one;
And though this may sound queer,
I search around and 'knock on wood',
'Tap! Tap! Tap! Tap!' I go;
And then I stop to listen
For a sound I always know.
It's my clever way of searching
For those grubs that live in wood;
No ear but mine can hear them -
No human's ever could.

I'm related to the mongoose,
The ring-tailed lemur, too;
But to those of little knowledge
I just scare them through and through.
I'm the strangest primate living,
With my ghostly orange eyes,
And with my spidery fingers,
I'm one scary big surprise.

And that's of course the reason why
In my own land I'm feared:
There's just one word describes me,
And that one word is ***weird***.

THE LONG NOSED BANDICOOT

I'm told that I'm endangered,
But some are worse than me;
It seems to be the case these days
For all those living free.
I have to fight both tooth and claw
All on my own, alone,
For that small nest of grass and sticks
We bandicoots call home.

Because of my long sniffy nose
I'm rather like a shrew,
But when you see me hop around
I'm like a kangaroo.
Of course I'm only little,
But my hind legs are quite long;
I use them when I have to fight,
And then to hop along.

I've a pouch to carry babies,
And I manage three or four,
But seven is a burden
And I cannot carry more.
I whistle and I grunt a lot
When hunting insect prey,
But that's at night-time only,
For I hide most of the day.

I know you won't forget my name,
It really sounds so cute;
Although there's many kinds of me,
All called a *bandicoot.*
But when you hear of bandicoots,
You'll know which one is *me:*
The long-nosed most endangered one
That you may never see.

We still live in Australia,
Though we're numbered as the few;
And although the law protects us,
That's as much as it can do.
A Bandicoot! A Bandicoot!
Please shout our name out loud;
It may sound very funny,
But it's one of which we're proud.

THE BUMBLEBEE BAT

I know for certain you'll never see
A bat as tiny and cute as me;
A bat that ranks with the small and great,
That weighs no more than a penny in weight;
A bat with the tiniest eyes to see,
A bat as small as a bumble-bee.

It seems the scientists all agree
There's no mammal living
Smaller than me.

I'm also known as the Hog-nosed bat,
You'll easily guess the reason for that:
My ears are so large they reach far out
In front of my head, beyond my snout.

A crowd of bats is a colony,
There are fifteen others as well as me;

Our hidden home is a joy to share,
It's nice to have such good friends there;
But I need some space to call my own,
So I don't hang close, I hang alone.
I eat my supper out on the wing,
A fly or two is a tasty thing;
And spiders that live on a nearby tree,
Also make a good meal for me.

Sadly we're all endangered now,
And the question everyone asks is *how?*
The answer lies in the land we share,
There's less and less for us living there;
It means less food can now be found
On all that grows upon the ground.

I come from places you may not know,
In secretive caves where rivers flow.
Where can you find me? I'll tell you where:
Thailand or Burma - you'll find me there.

But our numbers sadly are fading fast,
So nobody knows how long we'll last;
I counted each at my very last call:
One hundred and sixty left – that's all.

I know for certain you'll long to see
A bat as special and small as me;
And if man can manage to put things right,
And you are lucky – perhaps you might.

THE GHOST BAT

Although you'll find me in this book
Australia is the place to look
To get a real life view of me,
For that's the only place I'll be.

My spooky name of *ghostly bat*
Is scarcely to be wondered at;
I'm cloaked in fur of grey and white –
A most extraordinary sight!

And though I like the taste of meat
And there are creatures I will eat –
Don't think that I'm a vampire bat,
I don't suck blood or things like that.

I swoop down swiftly on my prey -
It has no chance to get away -
I wrap it round in wings so tight,
I only need to give *one* bite!

I fly to places that I know,
Where only bats like me will go:
A rocky place, a cave, a nook,
Where very few will think to look.

And should you ask what food I eat –
A mouse or bird would be a treat;
Look in my cave where I have dined,
And just their bones are all you'll find!

One of the reasons their numbers are declining is due to destruction
of their caves for mining.

THE BLACK BEAR

Of course you know I'm famous,
I'm the legendary bear,
And should you wish to find me
but you're not quite certain *where,*
You must try in North America
where I'm still roaming free,
Or over in Alaska, or Canada maybe.
If you meet me in the mountains
or down some forest trail,
I'll understand your feelings
if you turn a little pale,
For a bear can look *enormous!*
(You must make a note of this)
And is not the kind of creature
you can accidentally miss!

You might know of my cousin
the famous Grizzly bear,
It's lucky that we hardly meet –
for he gives *me* a scare;
I'm also very grateful that he rarely climbs a tree,
As whatever way you look at it,
it would be worse for me!
I'm a most proficient climber;
I climb each tree with ease,
Then eat the fruit and nuts I find,
as many as I please.
I rub my back against a tree;
I stand upon my toes,
And reaching high on my hind legs,
I rub it with my nose.
If another bear has been there first,
this is how I tell.
Experience is all one needs - plus a sense of smell.

As well as climbing trees with ease,
I also run quite fast;
I make the trees all crack and groan
as I go crashing past;
And did you know that bears can *swim*?
We really are quite good,
I'm sure you thought *"Well, fancy that!*
I never thought they could."
It also makes a welcome change
to try a different dish,
And if you meet me by a lake
I'll show you how to fish.

I make my den in hollow trees, or in a cave, or where
The undergrowth can shelter me;
I'll choose to make it there.
I began life in the wilderness and that is all I knew,
I learnt the things a bear must learn
and from a cub I grew.
Mother bears are strict, you know;
their patience soon runs out,
And cubs are always quick to heed
when mother gives a shout.
They're afraid they'll get a spanking,
that's why they always come;
But you'll know when one is happy,
for he gives a happy *hum.*

And now I've told my story:
how I swim, and climb a tree,
You'll say, *'Aren't bears delightful!'*
And you'll wish that you were **me.**

THE POLAR BEAR

'*A splendid sight*' I've heard you say,
Whenever I have passed your way;
But don't come close, is my advice,
I warn you - I won't tell you twice!

The largest of all predators
Still living on the land,
My height is equal to a *house*
When on two legs I stand.

I'm fierce, as everybody knows,
I think men are my only foes;
My coat is cosy, warm and white,
And though I **look** a real delight,
In the Arctic who would dare
To venture close to such a bear!

'A polar bear!' you cry, 'how sweet!'
'I wonder what he finds to eat,'
And if you haven't got a clue,
Just make a guess. It could be **you!**

As I'm sure most people know,
I'm camouflaged against the snow;
This means as I plod on my way
I'm not so easily seen by prey.
On floating chunks of ice I roam
Across my frozen Arctic home;
But ice has everything to give;
Without this ice I cannot live.

And all the ice is melting fast,
Much faster now than in the past;
It means less time to hunt, to eat;
To store up fat that gives me heat.
When sea ice melts and never stays,
A polar bear must fast for days;
And days will turn to months I fear,
And months might soon become a year.

Imagine if **you** had to wait,
And near starvation was **your** fate.
I know you'll say, *'It's such a shame -*
But global warming is to blame,'
Yet when you stop to think it through,
Much of the problem rests with *you;*
It's not too late to show you care -
Your help might save a polar bear!

THE SUN BEAR

I know I'm not a *good* bear,
I often get quite cross,
But that's because I'm small, and so
I like to show whose boss;
And should you come across me,
And shout in pure delight,
'A Sun Bear! Oh, I do declare!
A sweet and cuddly Honey Bear!'
I warn you, please take extra care,
I give a nasty bite!

The smallest bear of all bears,
I stand just four feet tall,
But when compared to other bears,
I've the biggest teeth of all!
I'm a very skilful climber,
With long claws on my feet;
And though it's often said I'm cute,
A Sun Bear doesn't just eat fruit;
A mammal has been known to suit,
A bird may taste as sweet.

In India, Indonesia,
And in Malaysia, too,
We Sun Bears still survive, although
We're threatened through and through.
We're an endangered species,
Please be aware of that;
With poaching comes our biggest fear
That all of us will disappear,
And then of course we also fear
Our loss of habitat.

If a tiger threatens me,
I'll make a barking sound;
And with my teeth and powerful jaws
I always stand my ground!
The natives call me *bear dog*,
In my leafy forest home;
You'll know me by my dark fur coat,
And on my chest beneath my throat
A patch of gold you're sure to note,
By which I'm named and known.

A poor and hunted little bear,
I'm under every threat;
Used for shameful practices,
Exploited as a pet;
It seems there's very little room
In my known world for me;
A bear with melting, pleading eyes,
Who, however hard he tries,
Is always seen as someone's prize,
Wherever he might be.

Of all the eight bear species,
Mine is least well known;
And this becomes the likely cause
Of why I stand alone.
My golden chest (so legend tells)
Signals the rising sun;
But hunters track me down at night,
They blind me with their flashing light,
And where my staring eyes shine bright,
They blast me with their gun!

They say I'm not a *good* bear
When I am fully grown;
I can't think *why* I misbehave,
Since Sun bears live alone.
But of one thing I am certain,
And I think you must agree –
The world will be a poorer place
If I should leave without a trace;
It would be such a sore disgrace
To lose a bear like me.

THE CANADIAN BEAVER

A master engineer, that's me,
Adept in everything I do;
I'm famed for my constructiveness,
And if my name requires a clue,
Think of the emblem I became,
When Canada preserved my name.

My industrious behaviour
In aquatics took me far;
The dams I build are works of art,
In fact I'm rated quite a star;
It's not as easy as it seems,
Shaping and diverting streams.

Any driftwood where I find it,
All along a river's length,
I mix and match with mud and stones,
To build my dam and give it strength;

My one first aim must be *defence,*
A strategy which makes good sense.

My front teeth cut the trees I need
For building, to construct my home;
And each new home is called 'a lodge',
A fact not always widely known;
A refuge where I hide from those
Fierce bears and wolves, my natural foes.

I've webbed hind feet for swimming,
And a tail that's flat and big;
I can use it like a rudder,
And my front hands help me dig.
I'm the biggest rodent in this land -
But a *gentle* one, you understand.

I don't eat fish, just leaves and plants,
Tree bark always tastes divine;
And when an enemy is near,
We beavers use a secret sign:
We slap the water with our tails
Before we dive; it never fails.

There were sixty million of us once,
Before the hunters came;
And still they trap us for our fur,
Despite our now exalted name;
But trade is less than in the past,
So hopefully the trend will last.

The otter shares my kingdom,
He's a relative to me;
And squirrel is my cousin -
Though he's always up a tree;
But beavers are of course the best,
And beavers are the cleverest.

So if you need an engineer
To clean your rivers; stop a flood;
Don't make yourself big problems,
Don't let yourself get stuck in mud.
Let someone do your work for free,
Remember – there is always *me*.

THE BILBY

I'm a desert dwelling bandicoot,
And Bilby is my name;
But as I'm sure we've not yet met,
I'll just try to explain.

In Australia where I come from,
I'm very scarce, you see,
So people soon devised a plan
To save the last of me.
"We'll call him *Easter Bunny,*
So he'll be loved a lot;
He's just about a rabbit's size,
Though a rabbit he is *not*."

A very good idea of theirs,
I really must agree,
Except that Easter bunnies
Look not a bit like me!

My snout is long and pointed,
I've a slender white tipped tail;
And the ears I have for hearing -
Well, I simply cannot fail!

They're gigantic, long and hairless,
Most extraordinary things;
You'd almost think they'd carry me
Through the air like wings.
They're very useful in the heat
And help to keep me cool;
As useful as my precious nose,
My marvellous 'sniffing' tool.

My eyesight isn't all that good,
So these things compensate;
And I hope - since I'm endangered -
Help doesn't come too late!

A Bilby is most comical,
I'm sure you will agree;
So *do* please find a photograph
And take a look at *me!*

THE BINTURONG

When people ask about me, I hear them all exclaim,
'Whatever is a Binturong? It's such a funny name!'
My common name is 'bear cat', but I'm neither bear nor cat,
I'm related to the mongoose. You have my word on that.

What countries do I live in? I'll name you quite a few:
There's Borneo and Burma; Sumatra; Java, too.

My whiskers are quite monstrous; eight inches it appears,
And I've funny little ear tufts much longer than my ears.
If you've met a sea lion face to face, I'm like him I suppose,
With my whiskers I have mentioned and my black and
shiny nose.

But my one great prime attraction is my most amazing tail,
And if I'm looking for attention, with this I cannot fail.
It's the same length as my body; so very thick and strong,
All covered in black shaggy hair that's beautiful and long.

It's what is called 'prehensile'; good for gripping onto trees;
I can *hang* with it, or *swing* with it, or *hold* things as I please.
A squirrel scrambles down head first as he descends a tree,
But *I* can play his game as well. Just watch me and you'll see.

I snort when I'm excited, or grunt or maybe hiss,
Or I'll howl up in the tree-tops. A sound you cannot miss!
I've a scent that's strange and wonderful, like *popcorn* I've heard tell;
The only creature in the world with that delicious smell.

I'm a little bit of lots of things. A weird and funny mix;
I guess that's why I'm able to perform unusual tricks.
I'll walk flat footed like a bear, but like a kangaroo
I'll balance (tail and hind legs) in this special pose I do.

So now when people ask you, *'A Binturong! What's that?'*
And *'What on earth's a bear cat? Is that half bear, half cat?'*
You can answer most politely, 'It's a most misleading name,
For he's rather like a mongoose but he's not *a bit* the same;
He's a little bit of grizzly bear, a bit of tiger cat,
But no-one seems quite certain - so I can't be sure of that.'

My name comes from Malaya, where I'm called a Binturong,
But as I'm still a *bear cat,* lots of people get it wrong!

THE BISON (AMERICAN)

I'm making a come-back (though it might be short time)
So I'm making the most off this status of mine.

I'm massive and mighty, an impressive great size,
With wicked sharp horns and red fiery eyes;
I've very few foes, but if we should meet
Don't forget, though I'm big, that I'm quick on my feet!
Only bears or a wolf pack can bring bison down,
I'm so huge and heavy; for that I'm renowned.

I once ruled America's great grassy plains,
Swept by warm winds with its sweet summer rains;
Here I was king, a great mammal from birth,
With mighty great herds, the biggest on Earth.
But I almost died out, due to man, long ago,
They killed us in millions I think you should know;
The ranch is my home now; the living is sweet,
Though the purpose I'm kept is to raise me for meat.

In park reserves only, you'll find some of me,
Though there's not many left of us roaming and free;
But in text books I'm mentioned (by experts who know)
As *a mighty great beast; a formidable foe!*

THE BUSH BABY

Do you know why they call me a baby?
It's because of my baby-like cries;
And I also look very much like one,
With my cute nose and saucer-like eyes.

I'm squirrel sized, cat sized, or mouse sized,
It depends on what species you choose;
And with so many new ones discovered,
A bush baby always makes news.

I'm the most prosperous primitive primate,
So I'm bound to be Africa's best;
And I know when you hear all about me,
You will quickly forget all the rest.
I've a tail I can see, that is longer than me,
I've round eyes that look like a cat's;
I've ears that can roll and unroll at will,
Gigantic in size - like a bat's.

I will chatter or croak; I will whistle or cluck,
Whenever I get in a fright;
Then using my tail in a powerful leap,
In seconds I'll vanish from sight!

In African forest I hunt through the night
For insects, or maybe just fruit;
But my diet will change with the seasons,
And I'll eat whatever will suit.
All through the day I will hide in the trees,
As I'm easily captured on ground;
I'm safe in a hole or a nest that I make,
In case eagles or snakes are around.

There are very few primates quite like me,
So please put me on top of your list;
With the loveable, quizzical faces I make,
If I vanish I know I'll be missed!

THE CAMEL

They say that I'm proud, that I'm lazy,
That I don't like to stand, but to sit;
They say that I have a bad temper,
And when I get angry I *spit!*
It's true that my manners are lacking,
And I know I am proud, but you see,
As the lion is king of the jungle,
The king of the desert is me.

I do things you would never imagine,
When I run – I can run really fast,
And I never get hungry for dinner,
It's clever the way I can last;
For my hump (which I carry above me)
Is where my provisions are stored,
So no matter how long my journey
I've always got plenty on board.

I've thick layers of lashes to cover my eyes
From the sand when a hurricane blows,
And I don't ever sneeze in a sand-storm;
I simply just close up my nose!
They call me *the ship of the desert*,
For I rock like a ship on the sea;
My walking might make you feel giddy,
If you travel the desert with me.

You ask how I walk without sinking
In the sand with all my great weight:
Each foot is made like a slipper,
As wide as a big dinner plate.
I can last for months without drinking,
And plod on my way quite content;
If food becomes scarce *I'll eat leather,*
Or bones – or my master's new tent!

There are special race days in the desert,
And my master is pleased if I win;
I become the most sought after camel,
And I earn lots of money for him.
But most days I'm loaded with luggage,
I'm expected to travel for miles,
And then they're surprised if I'm grumpy,
And not all politeness and smiles.

So when next you meet with a camel,
And you ride one who's rude - or won't go –
Remember the things that I've told you,
And you'll like him much better I know.

THE CAPYBARA

'*That*'s *a funny name,*' you'll say,
The moment you hear mine;
But if I just explain a bit,
I'm sure we'll get on fine.

I'm rather like a guinea pig,
A giant one - that's me!
And I'm also called a water pig;
Confusing I agree.
Of rodents I am quite the best,
No other is as big;
I'm quite the biggest in the world,
Maybe more *rat* than pig.

What's that I hear? Was that a gasp?
Or did you merely cough?
Just because I mentioned *rat*,
Don't let *that* put you off!
I'm really rather nice, you know,
I make a lovely pet;
I'll let you stroke and handle me;
You'll like me once we've met.

I speak in lots of different ways,
With whistles, grunts or squeals,
Whichever impulse suits me best,
Whichever most appeals.
I dive and swim in lakes and streams,
For that's where I belong;
But because I'm just a mammal,
I can't hold my breath too long.
I'll dive and stay down *minutes*,
In water that is deep,
And if I think I really *must*,
I'll stay down there to sleep!

Of course I really cheat a bit,
And as I move about,
If you look most carefully
You'll see my nose stick out.
My eyes and ears stay near the top,
When I go for a swim,
You'll recognize me straight away,
And shout, *'Yes, look! That's him!'*

I have a lot of enemies,
Like snakes, big cats, big birds;
It's really rather lucky
Capybaras live in herds.
We often lie on land to rest,
All basking in the sun,
But as soon as danger threatens,
We don't just dash and run:

We dive into the water,
And then, forsaking pride,
Unlike most other animals
We stay down there – and hide.

But when you're up the Amazon,
Or visiting Peru,
Don't forget to look for *me*,
And I shall look for *you*.

THE CASSOWARY

I'm not a bird that springs to mind,
About which people speak;
I'm from the age of dinosaurs,
An actual living freak.

Cassowary is my name,
A name not often heard;
One doesn't often tend to meet
A giant 'turkey' bird.

'You look quite pre-historic,'
Say most people that I meet;
'What huge and scaly legs you've got!
What big and knobbly feet!'

I make a kind of rumbling roar,
And then I move so fast,
You'll say, *'Was that a big school bus
That just went hurtling past?'*

I'm big, but not the biggest
Of any living bird;
Ostrich and Emu come before,
And I am counted *third.*

I run at most terrific speeds,
But then I cannot fly;
And you may never find me
Because I'm very shy.

I'm bald upon my head and neck,
But still I'm good to view;
You'll say, *'Now there's a handsome bird
With his top half painted blue!'*

I'm a great big feather duster,
In my brightly coloured dress;
But I'm not a very friendly bird,
I think I must confess.

Australia is my homeland,
Where I live with kangaroo;
But he's a far, far nicer chap,
If only people knew.

I expect you'll ask this question:
'What's that hard lump on your head?'
It's not a funny hat I wear,
But something you might dread.

It's my helmet that I fight with,
I butt with it, and ram;
It's a pity I'm so dangerous,
And not a friend to man.

I use my dagger claws to kick,
To slash with and to cut;
And my head of armour plating
Is like a coco-nut.

So now I give fair warning,
If ever we should meet:
I'm called *the world's most dangerous bird* -
You couldn't call *me* sweet!

THE COMMON CHAMELEON

When my name is once thought of, or mentioned,
The question arises *but why?*
And in case what you ask is exactly the same,
To answer I'll certainly try.

What does it mean *a chameleon?*
It's a mouthful you have to agree;
But the answer's surprising and rather beguiling;
You have to translate it to see.

It appears that the name is related
To the chamomile plant on the ground;
But chameleon also means *lion*,
A creature both loved and renowned.

So it seems I'm unique amongst reptiles,
Which should really create no surprise,
For of course what makes me so famous
Is my wonderful gift of disguise.

It occurs when the temperature changes,
I then turn to a quite different shade;
Or it happens with enemies lurking close by,
When I'm startled, or maybe afraid.

My tongue is another great asset
With which I am wonderfully blessed;
It's the same length as *me* when fully stretched out,
And it's sticky – I'm sure you'll have guessed.

I can blend in with ease to surroundings,
My colour will help me catch prey;
I simply sit still in a motionless mode,
Until something small comes my way.

It might be an insect or spider
Who's decided to just take the air,
When *whoosh!* there's a flash of my long sticky tongue,
And it's suddenly no longer there!

I'm a solitary creature I have to confess,
And though with my colours I tease;
It isn't much fun to sit hunched up all day,
And spend all my time in the trees.

I almost forgot, I must tell you,
There's another great thing I can do:
See *two* different objects at once with *both* eyes -
Or just *one* thing with *both* eyes – like you.

I don't like to boast (it's not manners)
But I don't think I've mentioned my tail:
It's long; it will grip; it's prehensile;
It will hold me as tight as a nail.

And now you must know where to find me:
The Mediterranean will do;
But all my exotic relations
Live as far off as distant Peru.

It would give me great pleasure to meet you,
But take care of the clothing you wear;
I might have a fright at your colourful sight,
And end up by tearing my hair!

THE CHIPMUNK

My first real name was *Chit-monk*
Which the Indians gave to me,
But the white man mispronounced it,
So it's really wrong you see.
I'm now just known as *Chipmunk*
And I'm the eastern kind,
Though there are over twenty more
I'm certain you can find.

I live in eastern Canada,
America as well,
And you'll know I'm not a squirrel,
For my stripes will always tell:
They're black and white, and brown and grey,
All down my back and head,
And then my hips, and rump and tail
Are lovely russet red.

You've guessed that I'm a mammal,
But I live upon the ground,
Not like some other look-alikes
That you may find around.
When I'm busy 'shopping',
I can store food in my cheeks,
But in winter time I hibernate,
And don't go out for weeks.

My appetite's enormous!
As well as nuts and seeds
There are eggs, bugs, mice and lizards,
On which a chipmunk feeds.
But my menu is much bigger,
There are slugs and insects too;
And other things not mentioned
Which are interesting to chew.

I make my nest in burrows,
In logs, and old stone walls,
And you'll often hear a chipmunk's voice
But never know he calls;
For I can chirp a bird's song,
And cry *'chip! chip! chuck! chuck!'*
But you will never guess that's me,
Unless it's just by luck.

In winter with my sense of smell
I search for nuts and seeds
Which once I hid in summer months,
When I had far less need;
It's nice to think that those I lose
Will someday sprout and grow,
And blossom into trees maybe,
Like those I see and know.

So when you think of chipmunks,
Just think about a tree,
And how it might have grown from seed
Once sown by little me.

THE COATIMUNDI

I'm a busy little creature with a greedy appetite,
And everyone who meets me
Says I fill them with delight.

You can call me *Coati* if you like or just *a hog-nosed coon*.
Coati is pronounced ko-WAH-ti
(I'm related to Raccoon.)

My full name *Coatimundi* is pronounced
ko-WAH-ti-MUN-dee.
Is there anyone you've ever met
Who has a name like me?

I live in Arizona and Argentina too;
And I troop around the forest
With my Coatimundi crew.

The rules are:
Raise your voices high whilst keeping tails erect,
And don't forget - protect your friends,
But keep the team select.

I said Raccoon's related - but for style there's little doubt
My body is more slender,
And *mine's* the longer snout!

Coati's are so clever when it comes to climbing trees;
As my ankles both reverse themselves,
I scramble down with ease.

I spend my day in foraging
for food of every kind:
Snails and ants, fish,
fruit and nuts,
Are some that I might find.

The Coatimundi Club we're called
by everyone we meet;
And I tell you that without us
No party is complete.

We're the long-nosed,
long-tailed mammals with
the most distinguished name:
Coatimundi! Coatimundi!
It's such a nice refrain.

You must try to come and see us if you ever get the chance,
But don't come uninvited,
You must warn us in advance!

Then we'll all come out to meet you with a Coatimundi game,
And you'll never want to leave us
To go back home again.

THE COLUGO

I'm called *a flying Lemur*,
But I've another name,
I'm *a Colugo* in Malaysia,
(I think they mean the same)
But I'm not a proper lemur,
And you won't believe it's true
When I tell you now quite honestly,
I'm related close to *you*.

I confess I don't *look* human,
Like an ape or chimpanzee;
But that's what all the scientists
Now finally agree.
I said I'm not a lemur,
And lemurs cannot fly,
I've just this special parachute
That helps me glide so high;
It's a long, thin, flowing membrane
Which behaves just like a sail,
Attached from neck to fingers
From my toes down to my tail.

Malaysia is my country,
Where I feed on leaves and fruits,
And flowers, if I find them,
Or leafy buds and shoots.
On every foot I've sharp curved claws,
For grasping after gliding;
I'm camouflaged in trees by day,
For then I'm always hiding.
My young are carried clinging
To my membrane as I glide;
You'd think I was a kind of bird,
With wings spread out each side.

I've other homes not mentioned,
And one's in Borneo;
But I'm possibly endangered,
And that - as you all know -
Will show that there are less of me,
And leaves me with the fear
I'll slowly vanish from your sight,
And one day won't be here.

You might say I'm peculiar,
That I look some kind of freak;
But when you really stop and think,
You'll find that I'm unique;
And when I steal on eerie wings
From trees at close of day,
You'll point and ask, *'Can they be bats -
Or just strange birds at play?'*

THE CROCODILE

Of all the reptiles you can name,
A crocodile is best;
I'm the largest living reptile,
And of course the cleverest;
I watch and learn what others do
When they're at work or play;
For animals and people do
The same things every day.

So if you're up the Amazon,
And feel you'd like a dip,
Or decide to do your washing there,
I'll give you just one tip:
Don't go there every day - same time -
Or that's when *I* shall go,
And I'll wait there for you patiently –
(As if you didn't know).

I'll creep up from the shallow end -
I've always had this knack -
And then I'll drag you down with me,
To make a tasty snack!
Of course it won't be pleasant,
But you're fair game, don't you see;
A croc eats anything that moves,
It's all the same to me.

Cold blood warm heart they say of me;
It's not one word a lie,
The *care* we crocodilians take!
And here's the reason why:
We guard our eggs most carefully
Once we have built our nest;
No-one can say a crocodile
Does not give of his best.

We work together as a team,
And surprisingly you'll find
The parents of our little ones
Are really very kind;
We carry babies in our mouth,
And, like a mother duck,
We teach them how to swim with us;
But then the rest is *luck.*

Just one in ten of hatchlings
Will reach their adulthood,
They have so many predators
Survival is not good;

Yet we've been around since dinosaurs,
I know for certain, though
We were of course much bigger then,
Millions of years ago.

We've hardly changed in all that time,
And when compared to man -
One hundred years (and forty more)
Is *our* allotted span.
So when you see our many teeth
We've had since time began,
Don't say that nothing frightens you:
A crocodile still can!

THE SPOTTED CUSCUS

I'm a spotted Cuscus,
Can you save me from a fate
That people call *extinction?*
This means I cannot wait
Too long for help to reach me –
And help might come too late.
My homeland is New Guinea,
And in Australia too,
It's possible you'll see me
If at first you have a clue:
I'm something like *a possum,*
But a spotted one it's true.

Many people also say
A monkey looks like me;
We have the same appearance,
And we both live in a tree;

So between him and the possum,
I'm the same, to some degree.

But there's another creature -
A sloth I'm told by name -
Who creeps amongst the branches,
And looks a lot the same.
It's all so very puzzling
And awkward to explain.

I'm spotted black and chestnut,
With body creamy white;
And with my legs of reddish-brown
I look a real delight;
But don't forget I'm rarely seen –
I'm only out at night.

A Cuscus isn't *tiny*,
You're in for a surprise:
A large domestic house cat
Would be about my size,
But *I* possess a special tail,
And lovely orange eyes.

My long tail grips the branches,
I can swing from it with ease;
It's always very useful
When I twine it round the trees;
You would call your tail *prehensile*
If you had one of these.

Fruit and leaves are mainly
The food on which I dine;
I reach them with my two-thumbed hands,
And five-toed feet of mine;
Four toes of which have giant claws
To help me when I climb.

I'm very shy of strangers,
I'm also very rare;
My home is disappearing fast,
And no-one seems to care;
So very soon if this goes on,
I'll simply not be there.

I'm a spotted Cuscus,
Can you save me from a fate
That people call *extinction?*
This means I cannot wait
Too long for help to reach me –
And help might come too late!

THE PYRENEAN DESMAN

I'm Europe's weirdest creature
Active only at night,
So to find me at all is the rarest delight.
I've waterproof fur - just watch me swim,
I'm a hotchpotch of oddities -
A funny sort of thing.

I've a body like a muskrat,
A long and wiggly nose,
And feet like a platypus without any toes;
I've big fine whiskers and little beady eyes,
There's not another like me,
I'm Nature's best surprise.

The Iberian Peninsula
Is where to search for me;
Or the Pyrenees (French side) that's where I'll be.
I live by mountains in fast flowing streams,

So trying to locate me
Is harder than it seems.

I'm a nocturnal creature
With a thick and scaly tail,
I use it for a rudder it's not a fish's tail;
And with my clever stylish snout
I probe around for worms and snails,
And then I dig them out.

In winter when it freezes
I live beneath the ice,
Where even for aquatics conditions are not nice;
I'm lucky that my burrows still can give me air,
But breathing is a problem
Of which I must beware.

Desmans are like windows
To man's most ancient past;
Can you save us? *Hurry!* We're disappearing fast!
We're rare – and rare means precious –
so don't forget our name,
If we're lost, we're lost forever,
And you must take the blame.

THE DOLPHIN

I'm a mammal - just like you,
I'm not a fish at all;
But no-one thinks that I'm a whale
Because I look so small.
Guess who's the biggest dolphin
That lives throughout the sea?
The answer might surprise you –
It's the *killer whale*, not me.

We dolphins welcome passing ships,
And dive and leap about,
Until the people wave to us,
And then we hear them shout:
'Look! What lovely dolphins!

Just what we hoped to see!
And oh, it's so much nicer
To see them swimming free!'

My tail, of which I'm very proud,
Is versatile and strong,
I use it when I'm hunting,
Not just to move along;
And when I need a breath of air
It helps to push me high,
So when my foe the shark I see,
I leap towards the sky!

But if I don't jump quick enough
And we should come to blows,
I have to do the best I can,
And fight with my long nose!
Of course I use my flippers too,
To steer me on my way;
They're also used to touch and stroke
My friends, when we're at play.

I do great stunts in leaping high,
Then diving down quite deep;
But the question everybody asks,
How does a dolphin sleep?

I sleep when I'm still half awake,
Or that's most people's view;
But really no-one's worked it out,
So no-one's got a clue.

I can't stay underwater long,
The way that all fish do,
Otherwise I'd drown because
I need air, just like you.

The sounds I make are little *clicks*,
I *buzz* or sort of *quack*;
And then my friends all do the same,
To call and answer back.
I whistle when I say 'hello',
And mothers whistle too,
When teaching little dolphin calves
To tell them what to do.

I enjoy your friendship greatly,
I can learn your ways with ease;
I'll do the most amazing tricks,
And try my best to please.
I can listen to the sounds you make,
And mimic words of yours,
No wonder I'm a creature
That everyone adores.

A dog - though he is clever -
Cannot puzzle problems through;
I'm as clever as some primates -
Though not quite as smart as *you.*

THE DORMOUSE

(One who sleeps)

Elusive is the word for me,
A creature you may never see.

For in a tree or on the ground
I'm very rarely ever found.
Dormir – to sleep – should give a clue,
It's something that I'm known to do;
And this I think should make it plain
That *Dormouse* is my common name.
My nest – if found – may give surprise,
It's like a tennis ball in size;
And there all day I'll curl up tight,
A tiny ball of gold and white;
By dusk I'm in my active state,
But don't forget I hibernate!

In summer I will nest in trees,
To feast on nuts I find on these;

In winter when the cold winds blow,
In hedge or underground I'll go,
And with my tail of fluff so fine
(No mouse can boast a tail like mine)
I wrap it round my curled up toes
To hide my head and warm my toes.
I'm someone secretive and small,
You'll hardly know I'm there at all;
But one day should you get the chance
To catch a glimpse – a fleeting glance
Of something wondrous to behold,
All softly coloured white and gold,
That sets your spirit winging free –
That's when you'll first set eyes on *me.*

With whiskers brushed and eyes shut tight,
I make a most appealing sight;
And when you see my fluffy tail,
To love me you can hardly fail.
I wrap it neatly round my head,
Then curl up in my cosy bed;
My long tail helps to keep me warm
Through wintry days of cold and storm.

I'm loved but very rarely seen
In Britain's countryside so green;
Large eyes, long whiskers – that is me,
No livelier mouse you'll ever see;
But dormice sleep well out of sight,
And only re-appear at night.
Amongst the trees I'll hunt for hours,
For fruit and pollen, nuts and flowers,

And that's why I'm so seldom found;
  I build my nest *above* the ground.
In summer that's the nest you'll find,
  In winter there's a different kind:
I build it then where wind can't get,
Well covered up from cold and wet.
And should you find my little home,
  I've fashioned like a ball or dome,
You'll see the bark that I have shred
  All softly lined to make my bed;
I might use wool I've found from sheep,
Or moss maybe, to help me sleep.

In Britain I'm the only kind
Of rodent very hard to find
In winter time. Because you see,
  No rodent hibernates like me.
But there's one creature I can name,
Who, though he does not share my fame,
  Looks and acts a lot like me,
And should be mentioned certainly.

The smallest mouse of any kind,
  Is little harvest mouse you'll find;
And just like me - his nest he weaves
  So cleverly from grass and leaves.
We're both of us endangered, rare,
With places loved no longer there;
Woodland practices have changed,
The farmland gone which once we ranged;
  One has to search most patiently
To catch a glimpse of *him* – or *me*.

THE FLYING DRAGON

I was here one million years ago,
When dinosaurs were here;
When fossil bones of me were found,
The evidence was clear;
There were bird-like things with talons then,
That flew from tree to tree;
And things with beaks that had no wings,
And there was little *me.*

Yet here I am again today,
Appearing much the same;
Except that now you'll find I'm called
By a more famous name.
But we dragons have a secret
We never like to tell;
It's something that is magical
And which is guarded well.

A lizard's *not* a dragon,
And a lizard's all I am;
But I'm one with this big difference,
I use this clever plan:
My ribs stretch out to form two wings,
With webbing in between;
It really is the cleverest trick
That anyone has seen!

I never fly; I jump; then glide
From tree to tree, to tree;
You have to watch most carefully
To see where I shall be.
If you go to Indonesia,
Across the China Sea,
You might be very lucky
And catch a glimpse of me.

I'm neither big nor fiery,
Like a dragon ought to be;
But *he's* the stuff of fairy tales,
Not true to life, like me.
So don't be disappointed
At my dragon's claim to fame;
You'll say when once you see me,
'You look just like your name.'

THE LONG
BEAKED
ECHIDNA

Most people laugh when meeting me,
and ask, *'Whoever's he?'*
For I *do* look quite an oddity I certainly agree.
I'm very like a porcupine with all the spines I've got,
But if you look quite carefully you'll see that I am *not.*

What really makes me different
is my very long, strange beak;
It's a subject of much interest,
about which people speak.

I find it very useful though it makes me look absurd;
Without my coat of prickles
you might mistake me for a bird!

I use my snout for foraging for food of every kind,
Ants are very tasty though to worms I'm more inclined;
I suck the ants up quickly –
since I sometimes *do* get stung,
But Echidnas have an extra tool; a long and sticky tongue.

I often sniff and snort a lot, and people think I'm hurt,
But I only snort and snuffle when my nostrils fill with dirt!

'The poor thing has a cold,' they say,
'that's why he snorts and blows,'

But they don't know how it tickles
when the ants climb up my nose!

Each baby we call *Puggle*; it's a name that's really cute,
And since we can't tell which is which,
the name is bound to suit.
The puggles live on mother's milk
and in her pouch they stay,
Until she digs a burrow
where she'll suckle them each day.

Papua New Guinea is where we long beaks live,
With all creatures weird and wonderful –
all those that I live with;
But the only mammals that lay eggs are Platypus and me,
And since you'll find we're both unique –
we're living history.

I've a very large and complex brain,
and yet - just stop and think -
I'm descended from the reptiles. Am I the missing link?
It's entirely unexpected in a mammal such as me,
So I'll understand if you're perplexed
as how I came to be.
I might have outlived dinosaurs – but how long will *I* last?
Please note that I'm endangered.
Don't consign me to the past.

THE ELEPHANT

My earliest ancestors lived here you know,
Some fifty-five million or so years ago;
They were woolly great monsters most fearsome to see,
Yet I'm led to believe they looked very like me.
I'm the largest land animal living today,
Though giraffe is the tallest, I hasten to say.

You might think you know all the things I can do,
But some things you might *not* - so here are a few:

I'll always remember you once we have met,
If you do me a kindness - I'll never forget;
If you ask me my age, I'll reply 'I'm not sure,
I can live 'till I'm *seventy* or a bit more.'
I'm as smart as a monkey or dolphin, you know,
I get wiser and wiser the older I grow.

My trunk is my pride; it can reach to my toes,
And this is so funny because it's my *nose!*
It's something to hug with when greeting a friend,
It's a dummy for babies who suck at the end;
I can use it for carrying, picking up things,
You cannot imagine the blessings it brings!
Unless you have got one you can't understand,
It's just like possessing an extra long hand.

I use it to breathe, and to eat … let me think,
I don't *drink* with my nose, but it *helps* me to drink.
I fill it with water, which tickles, and so
When I've sucked it all up - I just have to blow.
I can use it to dig me a wet muddy hole,
Where the flies cannot bite and where I can roll;
Then my friends hurry round and we all have a bath,
And we slide in the sludge, and we slither and laugh.

I'm lucky to have these big ears that I've got,
I use them to fan me when I'm feeling hot;
And then, as you know, I can swim if I choose;
I mean *under* the water! Now isn't that news?

When we start on a journey along a new trail,
We march like an army and follow each tail;
A baby clings tight to a tail that he knows,
And will follow his mother wherever she goes.
A tail is so useful to grip and hold fast,
When a crowd of relations comes hurrying past;
But then we might stop for a rest in the heat,
As we often find marching is hard on the feet.

The way that we do this is easy to learn:
First one leg is lifted, then each one in turn.

We elephants trumpet when angry or lost,
Or if some intruder our pathway has crossed;
The sound of us marching with loud tramping feet
Frightens off all those lions and tigers we meet;
But we're really quite gentle, protective and kind,
And help all our elephant friends that we find.
All that we ask is the right to roam free,
For it's cruel to confine such a giant as me.

The things that I've told you are perfectly true,
Did you know all the tricks that we elephants do?
As King of the Jungle I pass every test,
So forgive me for thinking 'an elephant's best.'

My underground den soon becomes really big,
Watch me shovel and scrape with my paws as I dig;
At night when it's cooler I'm out and about,
And I sniff everywhere with my sensitive snout;
If you ask what I eat, there is quite a long list:
Eggs, birds and lizards, I cannot resist,
And rodents and rabbits make very good meat,
Whilst a scorpion is always a succulent treat.

I keep a strict watch for an enemy, too,
There's a chance a hyena might loom into view;
Or maybe a jackal will creep softly by,
Or a vulture might drop like a stone from the sky.
My great ears detect every very small sound
Way up above me, or close to the ground;
While my long bushy tail - that is known as *a sweep*
Keeps my nose and feet warm whenever I sleep.

If you've searched for me often and always in vain,
The reason is simple I have to explain:
I'm mercilessly hunted and captured, you see,
A fate that is common for foxes like me.
I'm prized by the tourist; I'm sold as a pet;
I'm as rare where I live as a creature can get;
And though I delight each man, woman, and child,
It still does not answer my plight in the wild.

You might want to help me, but please, if you do,
Remember my home is *not* in a Zoo!
It's much more rewarding to see me run free
In the world I was made for, where I love to be.

THE FLYING FOX

I have a fox's face I'm told,
And since I seem to fly,
Someone silly called me *fox*;
As if a fox can fly!
I thought that I must tell you,
In case you asked me why.

I'm no relation to a fox,
Look closely and you'll see
I'm just a bat with giant wings,
A fruit bat – that is me.
But *flying fox* sounds grander,
I think you must agree.

Thirty million years ago,
I must have been around;
The fossils of my ancestors
Have just been lately found;
We are the largest bats alive,
For that we are renowned.

Our home is in Australia,
And Indonesia, too;

In remote and tropic islands,
Not known perhaps to you,
Where amongst the swamps and forests
Our numbers grew and grew.

We live in massive colonies,
There are millions of us there;
We don't venture into buildings,
Or caves, or houses where
There might be people living,
To give them all a scare.

We only feed on lovely things,
Like nectar; blossom; fruit;
That's why we always choose warm climes,
And only these will suit.
We'll forage up to forty miles
To find a tree to loot.

I'll grab a tempting branch I find,
Or hold it with my feet;
Then swinging upside-down, attached
With claws or my hind feet,
I'll draw the food towards my mouth,
And that's the way I eat.

So now you know a flying fox
Is no great mystery;
I'm just a bat with giant wings,
The biggest wings you'll see.
Call me *fruit bat* if you wish,
It's all the same to me.

BLUE POISON DART FROG

Hey! Watch out! Don't mess with me!
I'm small, as anyone can see,
A thumb-nail size to give a clue -
And brightly coloured – brilliant blue;
But don't come close – *and please don't touch!*
I cannot stress that point too much.
Of all most deadly creatures known,
It's often said I stand alone.

My diet is a poisonous kind,
And if you touch me you will find
That is the last thing you will do;
I'm full of poison through and through.
In Colombia's wildest parts
The Indians use it in their darts;
Blowpipes made and plied with skill,
From ancient times are known to kill.

In Suriname – I live there too –
Where once the wild wet forests grew,
Are 'islands' where you might find me;
I don't thrive in captivity.
But if a frog like me you meet,
You'll find no webbing on my feet;
I'm poor at swimming that is why
I like it wet – but also dry,
So streams are good to live beside
If there are stones where I can hide.

My jumping skills can't be surpassed,
You can't catch *me*; I jump too fast!
My lovely blue will make you stare,
But brilliant colours shout 'beware'!
Remember me – a frog that's *blue* -
But please don't touch! *I have warned you.*

THE GOLIATH FROG

You might believe that I'm that frog
Bewitched and in disguise,
Who is waiting for some princess
That he can claim as prize;
A frog just waiting for a kiss
She will (with luck) bestow
To change him to a prince again,
Like the story you might know.

But one day if you meet with me
You're in for such a treat,
For I'm no common sort of frog
You'll meet down any street;
I'm a frog of giant stature,
A 'goliath' frog – that's me,
The biggest found throughout the world,
You'll believe me when you see.

Imagine fifty million years -
Then add two hundred more,
And that's how long I've been around,
Before the dinosaur!
I begin life as a tadpole,
Like other frogs you know,
But then I never seem to stop,
I simply *grow* – and *grow*.

Goliath is a giant's name,
And I'm a giant frog,
As big as some domestic cats,
Or breeds of little dog.
I'll show you how to leap ten feet -
That's just three meters clear;
And since that's from a standing start,
It's bound to raise a cheer.

I come from Western Africa,
Where rivers once ran free,
Before man built the dams across
And cut down every tree.
We frogs I'm told, are good to eat,
And one the size of me,
Will make *three* courses in one meal,
With some still left for tea.

I have no voice to call to you,
Goliath frogs are mute;
And people harvest us for food,
Or keep us, since we're cute.

But adult frogs are highly prized,
And always prove their worth,
So soon there may be none of us
Of age to still give birth.

Of course all frogs are fabulous,
There's no such thing as *best,*
But since I was discovered
I tower above the rest.
I'm the *widest, longest, heaviest,*
With just one look you'll see -
And since I'm called Goliath,
I'll go down in history.

The world's frog population
Is fading without trace,
And like all creatures everywhere,
We're running out of space!
Apart from that, there's all those who
Collect us just for fun;
So the blame - as far as I can see -
Must rest with everyone.

I'm sadly now endangered,
So to show you really care,
Don't take me from the place I live;
Please kindly leave me there!

THE GHARIAL

If you've never heard of a Gharial,
Here's a chance for your taste to grow;
When improving your mind you will certainly find
How deplorably little you know.
I will cause you no fears though my jaws are like shears,
And people come many a mile
To stare eagle-eyed as I open them wide,
To show my most fabulous smile.
I'm a species of reptile you won't often find,
Much bigger than those of a similar kind;
In fact I am known as the biggest on Earth,
To give you some notion of what I am worth.

If you've never heard of a Gharial,
He's a kind of a crocodile
Who survives on *fish* – his favourite dish
That he eats only once in a while.
He snaps side-to-side with his jaws open wide,

Performing as if he's on stage;
For his super long snout that he thrashes about,
Grows thinner and thinner with age.
There's also a bulge at the end of his nose,
With webs on his feet between all his toes.
He cannot eat creatures much bigger than him,
Or anything large, since his jaws are too slim.

If you've ever heard of a Gharial,
You'll know that he's harmless to man;
But remember my name - for I came to fame
From the time when the reptiles began;
And though I'm not strongest, I live the longest
Of all other reptiles like me;
I'll swim, fish, and creep, where the waters run deep,
Where the rivers of India run free;
But now I'm endangered – and critically so,
Just think how you'd miss me if I were to go:
A croc that prefers a more elegant dish –
Whose slim jaws allow him to only eat *fish!*

THE GILA MONSTER

You pronounce my name as Hee-la,
I think you ought to know,
And I live in Arizona,
And also Mexico.
My bead-like scales look scary,
All yellow, red and black;
They say to predators *beware*
Be warned – I might attack!

I'm dangerous if, and when, I spit,
But before I act like this,
Although I'll sneak up quietly,
I'll warn you with a *hiss*.
I'll find you with my sense of smell,
Although I have poor sight;
And then I'll bite – and won't let go -
I'll *chew* as well as *bite*.

I eat frogs, mice, and centipedes,
And frogs and mice I'll kill;
But people, if they get a bite,
I just make rather ill.
I'm a shy, reluctant monster,
Lonely and seldom seen;
Living in desert burrows,
And rocks I hide between.

I'm slow moving, not ferocious,
And there's one thing I must add:
Because I'm not of monster size -
I don't think I'm *that* bad!

THE GIRAFFE

When people come to visit me,
They say, *'How quite extraordinary!*
What a most amazing beast,
He stands quite eighteen feet at least!'
No animal's as tall as me;
I'm the tallest in the world, you see.

On Africa's vast plains I roam,
That dry hot land that I call home.
My colour makes me hard to see,
I blend so well with grass and tree,
And with long legs that move so fast
I'm just a blur when I race past.

No-one I know can walk like me,
You really need to watch and see;
Two legs together mark my stride,
On first my right, then left-hand side;
No-one can reach me up so high,
I'll simply kick all those who try!

My favourite food is from the leaves
Of all the tall Acacia trees;
And here's another big surprise:
I'll poke my tongue out. *What a size!*
No, no, you haven't got it wrong -
It's *really* eighteen inches long!
It's black, and so extremely tough,
Sand paper would feel just as rough.

To stoop and drink I'm much too tall,
I'd topple and then quickly fall;
It makes you want to stop and think,
How *do* giraffes bend down to drink?
To reach down to the water side
I have to stretch my front legs wide,
And then my head eventually
Will just be low enough for me.

Giraffes can't cry or make a sound,
Or lie asleep upon the ground;
To lie and sleep is good and fine,
But how would I get up in time?
Imagine if I lay down still,

A lion might sneak up to kill;
And so when sleeping I must *stand.*
A safer bet you understand.

And just to give one more surprise,
I also sleep with open eyes;
So when a lion sneaks up to kill,
(As of course I know he will)
I'll show him what giraffes can do,
A thing that's always tried and true;
I'll show him legs that pack some power -
I'll run at thirty miles an hour!

People who see us close at hand,
(Depending on how close they stand)
Hope giraffes will bend down low
As far as their long necks will go;
Then what excitement, what a fuss,
They can't get close enough to us!
They clap their hands, they laugh, they shout;
They wave; they point, and jump about.

Then someone shakes their head and sighs,
'Oh, haven't they got lovely eyes!
Those lashes are what I would prize!
*I wish that mine were **half** that size!'*

THE GLIS GLIS

I am a Glis Glis. My name should be sung,
For I lived on Earth when the world was young;
I'm a rodent-like mammal, and you might not know
I came to Britain not very long ago.

He who brought me here, set me free,
And now I'm as happy as I can be;
I'll ransack your attic, raid every tree;
Chase me if you can – you can't catch me!

Though I *look* like a squirrel, looks can be wrong,
I'm just a large dormouse with a tail that's long;
People call me 'edible' they call me 'fat',
But I don't deserve bad names like that.

I'm up to all tricks, a precocious child,
Living in the Chilterns out in the wild;

I'll lodge in your roof or lurk in a tree,
But track me or trick me – *you can't catch me!*
Where I once came from - across the sea -
I was a great speciality;
They kept me in a jar, they fattened me up,
They served me as a dish for the Romans to sup.

People still farm me I have to say,
In a land called Slovenia - far away;
But here I'm protected and I run free,
So Britain is the place I love to be!

I'll run up your windows and then slide down,
Jumping and bumping, acting the clown;
I'll chew through wires and bite through wood;
I may look cute, but I'm never *ever* good.

'Woofle, woofle, woofle' hear how I speak;
A Glis Glis cry is considered unique;
But I'll lead you a dance wherever you may be,
And although you may try – *you won't catch me!*

THE SNOW GOOSE

A giant snowflake drifting
Where the atmosphere is thinned,
They call me *He who travels*
Beyond the wild North Wind.
I'll scarce be seen I fly so high
Through every kind of weather,
And tossed by storm, though blizzards rage,
We snow geese fly together.

From warmer climes we travel
All night and through each day,
Three thousand miles towards our home –
And some fall by the way.
Upon the Arctic tundra
We colonise to nest,
Each nest lined with feathers
Plucked from a female's breast.

Arctic foxes welcome us,
Wolves and eagles, too;
And though we males defend our eggs,
We always lose a few.
Each gosling born in summer
Must swim and dive when small,
To gain the strength much needed
For their long flight in the fall.

We gather in our thousands
When autumn has begun,
In flocks so vast and awesome
That we cover up the sun;
A cloud of white, a snowstorm
That rolls across the sky,
Is all that human eyes discern
When snow geese fly so high.

From bleak Siberia's lonely wastes –
A theft free paradise –
We cross the wide white glaciers
And endless fields of ice;
Then southwards far across the sea
We take the path we know,
Onwards to America –
As far as Mexico.

Here the rice fields offer food,
The prairies grass and grain,
And here we stay till early spring
When we must leave again;

We'll then migrate a *second* time
To take those routes we've known,
And with the instinct that we have,
'To nest' means 'coming home.'

Alaska, Greenland, Canada,
These three my kingdoms are;
But not *all* who take that journey
Will make it out that far;
The rushing of our passage
Is a noise that fills the air,
A sight to lift a weary heart,
A sense beyond compare.

Onwards – ever on I go:
Weak, weary, wracked with pain,
And if I don't fall by the way,
I'll make it home again.

THE MOUNTAIN GORILLA

They call me the Gentle Giant,
And though when my picture you see,
You might say, *'he looks quite ferocious,*
He looks most aggressive to me,'
Really my looks are deceiving,
I'm quiet, retiring, and shy,
I don't beat my chest very often;
If I do, there's a good reason why.

I do it whenever I'm threatened,
To show that I'm stronger than you;
And of course though I've no wish to hurt you,
It's done to make *you* frightened too.

In Africa, that's where you'll find me,
But please never point or just stare;
I might think you've come to cause trouble,
And mistake your stare for a *glare.*

I make lots of noise when I'm frightened,
I'll throw things, and then what is more,
I'll stick out my tongue as rude as can be,
And chase you away with a roar!

I often stand upright on two legs,
It really depends who's around,
But I usually walk in my own hunched up way,
My long arms just touching the ground.

I climb trees but not very often,
Though leaves, fruit and seeds are a treat;
And as you can guess it's quite handy
To hold things with both hands *and* feet.

Though I can't help looking so ugly,
You'll see if you look in my eyes
A soulful, appealing expression,
That's trusting and child-like, yet wise.

A chimpanzee is quite different,
And it's perfectly true he can swim;
But I grunt, I growl, I chuckle and hoot,
And I make and use tools just like him.

I'm shy (as I've said) and not cheeky,
Like my cousin the chimpanzee;
But as I'm the last of the world's great apes,
There's no-one as special as me.

Yet I'm hunted here in my forest home,
The only home that I know;
And with almost all of my trees cut down,
I ask you - *where can I go?*

There will soon be none of us big apes left,
Our numbers are pitifully few;
We hardly remember the world we loved,
Caged and confined in a Zoo.

Please put my name at the top of your list -
A gorilla is clever *and* kind;
And I am the primate closest to man
Of any that you'll ever find.

THE HIPPOPOTAMUS

I know that my waist is enormous,
And I look so disgracefully fat;
But I'm told that I look like a *barrel*,
And there's surely no reason for that!

It's true that I *do* enjoy eating,
And I sleep all the day I'm afraid,
But that's nothing to do with my figure;
That's the way that a hippo' is made.

My river is lovely to doze in,
The best place of all to keep cool,
And guess what my treat is to follow?
A roll in a deep muddy pool!

Did you know I can roar like a lion?
But of course my biggest surprise
Is the fact that my nose is on top of my head,
And so are my ears and my eyes!

It's handy for keeping a look-out,
I can see, breathe, and listen with ease;

And with only my eyes, nose and ears sticking out,
I think I am rather a tease.

I can play lots of tricks underwater,
That's something not everyone knows;
And just to make certain no water gets in,
I can close both my eyes *and* my nose.

I can walk on the bottom of rivers,
And touch it with every big toe,
And though I am big and so heavy,
I run faster than *you* - did you know?

Baby hippo's are born under water,
Though they've no inclination to stop;
For to take their first breath the poor little things
Must swim all the way to the top.

Night- time's the best time for hunting,
We hippo's need truckloads to eat;
And I'll munch fifty kilos of green stuff,
(It's no wonder I can't see my feet)!

My mouth is enormously monstrous,
But be warned when I open it wide,
It means that I'm terribly angry -
And you'd better run quickly and hide.

I'm one of the heaviest creatures,
But the experts it seems can't agree
Which one of us two is the biggest,
My old friend Rhinoceros - or *me.*

THE SPOTTED HYENA

I'm cunning and I'm sneaky,
But isn't it a shame
That because of these bad habits
I must always take the blame?
For a lion (if you watch him)
Will steal another's kill,
But *my* reputation clings to me,
I think it always will.

I wait and watch most patiently
While others do the work,
I circle round, lie down a bit,
And generally *lurk;*
I pretend that I am leaving,
(It's a kind of 'waiting' game),
Then when my prey is sleeping
I will grab him just the same.
There's never any wastage,
Each whole body I'll digest:
The bones, the hair; the horns, the teeth,
I eat them with the rest.

What country will you find me in?
I'll give you just one guess.
Did I hear you say South Africa?
That's right, that's my address.
And what do I remind you of?
A cheetah, dog, or bear?
With front legs longer than the back,
It's harder to compare.
I'm related to the mongoose,
I'm closest to a *cat*,
(I thought that might surprise you)
For I don't look much like that.

I look a bit like camel,
But I walk like the giraffe,
And I laugh mad human laughter.
Have you heard hyenas laugh?

'Har-hee-hee! Ha-i-e-na!'
It's an eerie, scary laughter,
I giggle, cackle, whoop,
And it always sounds more awesome
When I sing within a group.
'That's him,' you'll say, *'the one with lots
Of the most delightful spots!'*

Please remember the hyena,
(He's far smarter than the rest)
And everything hyenas do
They always do the best!

THE HYRAX

I'm rodent-looking, rabbit sized,
So not exactly big;
And those who see me often say
I'm like a guinea-pig.
I take my name from place names,
And there are always three:
Whichever place I choose to live,
By rock, by bush, or tree.
Forty thousand years ago,
I was still around
Across most parts of Africa,
Where today I'm found.
The little pads upon my feet
Are there to help me climb;
I jump and dive, and twist and turn,
I'm active all the time.

I can't control my body heat,
So in the colder weather
Each hyrax seeks a brother's warmth,
And cuddles close together.
My ancestors were elephants,
And also manatees;
But *teeth* are all that now remain
Of tusks I had, like these.

I've lots of secrets you won't guess,
Like staring at the sun;
And people think I'm blind – but no,
I'm fooling everyone!
My eyes are well protected,
I'm a mammal that's unique;
And have you heard the noise I make?
I don't just merely *squeak.*

I *sing* when I am happy,
I sing to get a mate;
And every kind of grunt I give,
Decides my future state:
I begin with lots of wailing,
And end with one long snort;
Its quality and frequency
That count, as well as thought.

I can roar loud – like a lion,
And when climbing, if I fall,
No matter how high that may be,
I'll not be hurt at all.
I'm really quite a mystery
In many things I do;
And though the desert is my home,
I live in forests too.

I'm mentioned in the Bible
As a creature small and wise,
Who, though he has but little power,
Looks upward to the skies.

I watch for birds high on my perch,
Or snakes that sometimes climb;
Of leopards too, I must beware,
For they're no friends of mine.

I'm almost vegetarian,
It's mostly plants I eat;
Though I'll maybe take a lizard,
Or a bird's egg for a treat.
My moisture comes from leaves and fruit,
And berries that I find;
I very rarely need to drink,
Like others of my kind.

I might give the impression
That I'm lazy and I'm fat;
But when you see how fast I move,
You'll soon forget all that!
I'll be gone in just a second,
Whenever danger's near;
There's more to every one of me
Than would at first appear.

There are animals in Africa
More spectacular by far;
And some are big, and some are fierce,
And some are quite bizarre.
But the hyrax is a mammal
Unlike any other;
Just think about an elephant,
And remember – he's my brother!

THE JAGUAR

Just the mention of my name
Conjures up a host of things;
Grace and beauty, awesome strength,
A symbol used by kings.
In ancient temples once I walked
Silently by golden throne,
Worshipped by those living gods
All crumbled now to dust and bone.
A leopard might confuse you,
But look closely and you'll see
Our markings are quite different,
Although he looks like me.
My patchwork coat has dark rosettes,
Gold threads between the knots;
And on each centre-piece you'll see
A jaguar has *spots.*

Jaguars are also black,
And so are leopards, too;

But my large head and forelimbs
Will help you guess who's who.
My name means *one who kills its prey*
With just one single bound,
And though I'll pounce down from a tree,
I mostly hunt on ground.

A tiger's bigger than a lion,
And I come third in size;
But having proved my awesome strength,
I'm seen as quite a prize.
I'm rare in the Americas,
But you will find me still
In forests of the Amazon,
And countries round Brazil.
The crocodile feared only man,
Until he met with *me;*
I'll search a shallow river spot,
Then wait, crouched in a tree;
And once I see him swim below,
I'll pounce upon his head,
Then pin him to the bottom
And drown him till he's dead.

No other big cat catches fish
As often as *I* do;
My jaws can pierce a turtle's shell,
And crush it through and through.
No other creature but for man,
Would dare to challenge *me;*
I have no need to carry prey
And hide it in a tree.

Once worshipped as a god I was,
For courage, strength, and power;
Yet now I'm fighting just to live,
Each moment, every hour.
I'm vanishing so quickly
Before I'm fully known;
The shyest and least understood
Of cats that hunt alone.

I fight for space to hide or hunt,
To stay just where I am;
And the loss of all my habitat
Is entirely due to man.
The land once wild, no longer is,
With forest cover all but gone;
And poachers come to trade my fur.
What can I do? I just move on.

THE LESSER JERBOA

Whatever is a Jerboa?
You haven't got a clue?
Some people say I look quite like
A baby kangaroo.
It's true I'm only mouse-sized,
But oh, how I can hop!
And once I've started on my way,
I find it hard to stop.

You'll never ever catch me,
Unless I'm fast asleep;
For every stride a human takes,
I'll do *four* in one leap!
My hind legs are for jumping,
They're long, as you can see;
My short arms are to hold my food,
And makes sense you'll agree.

I sit and balance with my tail,
It's twice as long as me;
But that's what makes me different
From rodents you may see.
Because I eat both plants and meat,
I'm called an 'omnivore';
But a beetle is the biggest thing
I'll eat with *my* small jaw.
In North Africa or Asia,
Where I'm certain to be found,
I burrow deep to make my den,
In sandy, stony ground;
And if it's cold in winter,
I'll sometimes hibernate;
And in the heat I'll do the same,
Just simply sleep - and wait.

You'll very rarely see me,
But when the sun goes in,
If you happen to be lucky,
You'll say, *'Oh look! That's him!*
How very sweet and small he is!
How big and black his eyes!
And see his long and tufted tail?
It's almost twice his size!'

I'm not unlike a little mouse,
With hind legs very long;
But *my* name is *Jerboa,*
So please don't get it wrong.

THE LONG-EARED JERBOA

I know you'll say, *'I've met with him -*
He's on a previous page,'
But *I'm* the species making news,
So I'll take centre stage.
I've just been caught on camera
As 'the mammal most bizarre',
So people rush to see me,
And they come from near and far.

My ears - of such enormous size -
Are my real claim to fame,
So *Mickey Mouse* or *Big Ears*,
Would make a good stage name.

Three times the size of my small head,
A wondrous sight they are -
That's why I've hit the headlines,
And I'm now a movie star!

They help to spread my body heat
Whilst hopping on the ground
In the rocky Gobi desert,
Where I can still be found.
My cousins out of Africa
Have little mouse-like ears,
You'll quickly see the difference
For mine are *rabbit's* ears!

I've captured hearts world-wide it seems,
And all for one good cause;
I'm one tiny threatened creature
That everyone adores.
I'm distantly related
To all creatures known on Earth,
Yet few had even heard of me,
And none had guessed my worth.

But I'm marked as one of many
That deserves consideration;
All creatures weird and wonderful
In need of conservation.

THE KAKAPO

You'd never tell just from my name
What creature I could be;
And since I've no close relatives,
There's no-one quite like me.

I'm the world's one flightless parrot,
Because (you might not know)
I had no predators to fear
Millions of years ago;
And since I had no need to fly,
I did not even try;
So soon my wings were powerless,
And could not lift me high.
Instead, I parachute from trees
That I have learned to climb,
Using my wings for balancing -
A trick uniquely mine.

New Zealand is my only home,
And maybe you have heard,
I'm important to the Maori -
I'm their legendary bird.

I was moved for my protection
To my off-shore island home;
Two islands – to be quite precise -
Where now I'm free to roam.

I'm the only parrot living
That is active just at night;
And that's the meaning of my name,
Parrot of the Night.
My mating call is very deep,
A sonic boom you'll hear;
But since I'm such a fussy bird,
I do not nest each year.
I only breed when special trees
Can give me fruit to eat;
And since I have to climb them first,
That fruit is quite a treat.

Of all the parrots in the world
I weigh the most, it's true;
And I'm certainly the *biggest,*
The longest living, too.

I'm the greatest treasure, surely,
In this country of my birth;
But I'm also sadly listed
With the last that's left on Earth.
I'm fighting for survival
With the help of those who know,
So, please tell the world about me;
My name is *Kakapo.*

THE TREE KANGAROO

"You really must be joking!"
That's what they say of me,
"A kangaroo that leaps from trees!
That simply cannot be!"

All those so high and mighty
who think themselves so wise,
Will have a shock when they find *me;*
Imagine their surprise!

I'm a little bit of monkey; I look a bit like bear;
I'm secretive; mysterious;
I'm endangered, a*nd I'm rare!*

You don't know where to find me?
You haven't got a clue?
Try Australia or New Guinea,
And I'll show you what I do:

The huge and awesome leaps I make,
a monkey wouldn't dare;
You'll see me fly a hundred feet,
As I dive through the air.

I've got a long and furry tail that balances me well,
But it won't grip trees (like monkey's tail)
To hold me if I fell.

I might *live* like a monkey but I'm more like kangaroo,
With a pouch to carry joeys in,
Like kangaroos all do.

I'm related to the kangaroo.
I think that must be plain,
But as I'm also monkey-like,
I don't know *who's* to blame.

It seems I'm just a miracle that somehow came to be;
But of one thing I'm quite certain,
You'll not find another *me.*

I'm very well adapted to my life among the trees,
Where I eat the fruit and flowers,
Play at hide-and-seek, and tease.

One moment you will see me; the next I will be gone;
And that's what might become of me
If things just carry on.

My trees are disappearing,
I'm still relished as 'a treat';
You won't believe – but yet it's true,
I'm hunted *just to eat!*

It's no wonder that I like to stay
well hidden out of sight,
But now you've heard my story,
My future might be bright.

You'll tell the world about me and all the things I do;
And people won't believe at first
I'm called *a kangaroo.*

THE KANGAROO

My name is rather long I think,
That's why they call me *Roo;*
But *Kanga* is my other name
That's short for Kangaroo.

I've got a lovely long thick tail
For balance when I hop,
And once I get up lots of speed
It's difficult to stop.
My tail is good for steering,
And for slowing down you see;
It's really like an extra leg,
Most useful, you'll agree.

To say I do not drink for *months*
With all my exercise,
In a hot land like Australia,
Might come as some surprise;
But I dig big holes for water,
Which is clever don't you think?
And when I've dug one really deep,
Then all my friends can drink.

Sometimes I grunt and cough a bit,
And then sometimes I fight;
And with these strong hind legs of mine,
I kick with all my might.
I'm good at boxing! Give me gloves
To cover my sharp claws,
And watch me fight! I'm really good
At punching with my paws.

Our babies are such tiny things,
Born small as honey bees;
You wouldn't think a kangaroo
Was once as small as these.
They live within a mother's pouch,
Where they are fed and nursed;
Each pops out to view the world,
And then pops back - head first!

Oh, kangaroos are clever,
But there's one thing we can't do;
We find we can't walk *backwards,*
We don't know why. **Can you?**

THE KINKAJOU

I'm a Kinkajou! A Kinkajou!
It's such a lovely name;
It sounds just like a magic spell,
A riddle or a game.
You pronounce my name as *Kink-a-choo*,
It really is such fun
To have a name to play with
That can puzzle everyone.

A conjurer might use it
When I'm hiding up a tree,
And when he waves his magic wand
You'll suddenly see *me.*
You might say I remind you of
A monkey or a cat;
I'm sometimes called *a cat monkey*
Because I look like that.

Really I'm a small raccoon,
But one most hard to find;
There's not another like me,
I'm a most unusual kind.

People call me *honey bear*
Because my special treat
Is the nectar that my tongue can reach
From flowers that I eat.
My fur is coloured golden brown,
So that's another clue

As to why I'm nick-named honey bear,
For bears love honey too.

You'll find me in the Amazon,
In forests dark and deep,
In tree holes where I'm hard to find,
And where all day I sleep.
But if you search for me by night,
You'll get one big surprise,
For all you'll see between the leaves
Will be my shining eyes.

Try and catch me if you can,
A Kinkajou moves fast!
You'll shout, *'There goes his long, long tail!'*
As I go leaping past.
It's a lovely warm and fluffy tail
For snuggling down to sleep;
For clinging with, for hanging by,
For balance when I leap.

I'm secretive and very shy,
And as most people know
You rarely see a Kinkajou,
Except his nose - or toe.

I'm a Kinkajou! A Kinkajou!
My name is such a treat;
I'm sure that you'll remember it
If we should chance to meet!

THE KOALA

I'm Australia's favourite animal,
The cuddly Koala bear;
Except that if the truth be known,
A Koala's *not* a bear.

My nearest best relations
Are my old friend Kangaroo,
(And that funny fellow, Wombat),
Which means that I have *two.*

My name is Aboriginal,
And *koala* is a word
Which means 'no drink' by all accounts,
Or that is what I've heard.

All that I need for food and drink,
I get from just one tree,
(And though you might think that's a bore)
It's still a treat to me.

There's six hundred of these luscious trees
Of Eucalyptus fame,
And each one looks quite different,
And not one tastes the same.

My babies, like the kangaroo's,
Are all called 'joeys' too;
They cannot *see* or *hear* when born,
But guess what each can do?

Although they are the tiniest things,
Just like *a bean* in size,
Each must reach its mother's pouch,
Or left outside, it dies.

The task seems quite impossible,
The journey far too long,
But the joey climbs and then he crawls,
For his hands and feet are strong.

Then once he's reached his mother's pouch,
He snuggles down inside,
And there he'll stay for six long months,
To sleep, to feed - and hide.

And when at last he grows too big,
He simply learns the knack
Of holding tight with hands and feet,
To ride on mother's back.

There's not so many left of us
Who still live in the wild,
So help us to survive and thrive,
Each woman, man, and child.

If you think I'm slow and sleepy,
That's not because I'm rude;
A koala needs more sleep than you,
And *time* to digest food.

I'm a quiet friendly creature,
And I rarely make a noise;
I mean no harm to anyone,
I'm one of Nature's joys.

There's just one thing remaining
I would whisper in your ear,
But I shouldn't really whisper -
I should shout it loud and clear:

'A koala's a marsupial!
He's a creature that's quite rare;
Please don't forget to tell your friends,
*A koala's **not** a bear!'*

THE KOMODO DRAGON

I'm the monster of adventure tales - the ancient and the new,
And though you'll say *there's no such thing!* I happen to be true.
I don't breathe fire like dragons, neither can I fly,
But should we meet and you feel faint,
Well here's the reason why:

I've scaly armour plating and a tail that's like a knife,
Much longer than my body size,
I swing it like a scythe!
I'm related to the crocodile, the alligator too;
And maybe you have guessed the truth,
Or you already knew:

I'm really just a lizard. But a lizard of some worth;
The most dangerous, most ferocious,
The biggest found on earth.
Komodo Island is my home, and there as king I reign,
With about five thousand others
Of Indonesian fame.

You might think I cannot chase you; that a runner I am not;
But though you might outlast me,
Outrun me you will *not!*
I'll run much faster than a man - at twenty miles or more,
And if I get within good reach,
You soon will be no more!

The Komodo is cold blooded, and from my hidden lair
My babies hatch like snakes from eggs,
Then breathe to take the air.
We hunt for fish and birds of course, and don't make any fuss,
But bigger prey like buffalo,
Are what really interest us.

I'll eat wild boar, a monkey, or a smaller one of *me*;
I'll eat most anything that moves
That lives on land or sea.
So many things have bitten me it's no surprise you see,
To think that every bite I've known
Is reproduced in *me.*

I can poison with my tainted mouth or pierce you like a lance,
And all I ask for you to do
Is give me half a chance.
I hope you'll visit very soon this land that bears my name,
I'll welcome you with open jaws,
But you may not leave again!

I'm the Dragon of Komodo, and before each day has dawned
I leave my lair to eat my fill.
Remember ... *you've been warned.*

THE RING-TAILED LEMUR

You don't know what a lemur is?
I'll tell you if I can;
I'm a kind of primate, like an ape,
A relative of man.
You'd never guess it by my looks,
Or my long pointy nose;
You'd laugh to see me upside-down
Just hanging by my toes!

There is an island where I live,
An island of my own
Not far off from Africa,
That is my only home.
And there I spend long lazy hours
Sunbathing in a tree,
Turning myself from side to side
To warm both parts of me.

To come across me suddenly
Might cause you some surprise;
A creature with the strangest tail,
And such big yellow eyes.
My tail has rings of black and white,
My eyes are ringed black, too;
And yet my babies, every one,
All have eyes of blue.

When lemurs want to say hello,
We wave our tails about;
We also wave to signal
There's danger! Please watch out!
All higher ranking males you'll find
Strut round with heads held high,
And pass with noses in the air,
Tails raised towards the sky.
The lower ranks of course, look down,
And drop their tails down, too;
They have to do as they are told,
Like all the youngsters do.

But of all the lemurs in our group
That you may come across,
A lady lemur reigns supreme;
A lady is the boss.
She always wins an argument,
She chooses her own mate;
And of the others you could say,
They're simply second rate.

Each mother carries in her mouth,
Her baby ball of fluff,
And each will ride upon her back
Once it is old enough.
Mothers also care for those
Babies not their own,
And nurse them till the little ones
Are almost fully grown.

The meaning of our name is *ghost,*
And with our staring eyes
And haunting sounds we make at night,
We're proud of our disguise.
We can purr and mew like house cats,
But our favourite claim to fame
Has always been our lovely tails,
From which we take our name.

THE SNOW LEOPARD

I'm difficult to find and track,
I'm elusive and so shy
That I've become a legend,
And here's the reason why:

Snow leopards are the rarest things,
Magnificent to see,
But as there are so few of us,
We're making history.

The Himalayan Mountain range
Is one place where I roam;
Amongst the craggy snow-capped peaks,
I travel all alone.

I live in alpine meadows too,
In China, Pakistan,
In India, and in Russia,
Where I seldom see a man.

A descendent of the Saber-tooth,
Sabu is my name;
A name the locals gave to me
Before the hunters came.

I'm called *the phantom ghost cat*
Since I'm so rarely seen
Amongst the rocky wilderness,
In my coat of white and cream.

At dawn and dusk you'll find me,
For then I seek my prey:
Wild sheep and goats, and hare and deer;
But then I sleep by day.

My long soft coat of thickest fur
Protects me as I go,
Wandering amongst the peaks
Of mountains deep in snow.

I'm different from the tiger cat,
You will not hear *me* roar;
But just one growl, one cough or bark,
Will shake you to the core!

No other cat has such a tail,
So long; so thick; so warm;
A blanket made to cover me
In raging wind and storm.

It also helps to balance me
On dizzy rocky heights;
To see me leap a great crevasse
Is one of life's delights.
My furry feet, like snowshoes,
Are made to walk on snow,
Like the great pads of the lynx cat,
Who treads where I might go.

I'm wary and elusive
To a magical degree;
But even with my camouflage
Man dares to still hunt me.

Most mysterious, most beautiful
Of all big cats on earth,
Surviving in such hostile climes;
How *can* one count my worth?

Few humans will have seen me,
Though they will always try;
And after all I've told you,
You'll know the reason why.

THE ASIATIC LION

Although I'm called the King of Beasts,
I'm not the biggest cat;
The tiger is the first in line,
And he lays claim to that;
But as a symbol strong and brave
The lion stands alone.

On shields and flags my symbol flew,
When kings rode out to war;
And those who saw it fled in dread,
Like all who heard me roar;
And still I'm known as *lion heart*,
And still I stand alone.

A tiger slinks by quite unseen,
A lion stands his ground,
Curious but unafraid,
For this he is renowned.
He's not as other great cats are;
The lion stands alone.

My cousins out of Africa
More fortunate by far,
Are not on the endangered list
As Indian lions are;
Here we stand upon the brink,
The last of us, alone.

A lion likes to socialise
Once he is fully grown;
We greet our friends by rubbing heads,
So each by scent is known;
And by this act of comradeship
The lion stands alone.

A lion works with all the pride
To stalk and ambush prey,
He'll bring down prey *three* times his size,
In his own resourceful way;
For in the art of strategy
The lion stands alone.

As the male most dominant
I rarely lift a paw,
Unless the prey should prove too big,
And the pride can do no more;
And then the call goes out to *me*
To battle on my own.

As King of Beasts I strike a pose,
I laze, all duties shirk,
And leave my mate to rear my young,
To hunt and do the work;
For as the male most dominant
I rarely leave my throne.

Whilst the females do the hunting
And then bring home the kill,
I sit and look majestic,
Though I'm *first* to eat my fill.
And that's the way it should be,
For a lion fully grown.

I'm extremely territorial,
And should I meet a man,
A leopard, or a cheetah,
I'll kill one if I can.
A lion needs a lot of space
That he can call his own.

Because I'm now so crowded
Into territories so small,
Of all big cats in India
I'm the rarest of them all;
And the race is on to save me,
In this land I still call home.

My symbol stood for Justice,
For Freedom that once was,
Emblazoned on an ancient flag
Once proudly flown, because
As the privilege reserved for kings,
The lion stands alone.

THE FRILLED LIZARD

People cry, *'Just look at him!*
What a frightful monstrous thing!'
And photographs you take of me
Will cause most people to agree.

Though I may scare you through and through,
It's just a trick to frighten you;
It's quite unique and very clever,
It really is the best trick ever!

Around my neck I have this frill
That I can open wide at will;
It's brightly coloured – quite a size,
And bound to give a big surprise.

I use it when I run from harm,
To frighten or to raise alarm;
So when I'm active in the day,
My enemies will run away.

And should you ask me what I eat -
Crickets always make a treat;
Mammals (if they're small) will do,
And spiders I am partial to.

In Australia you will see
My colour matches land and tree;
And though I'm big (if treated right)
I promise I will rarely bite.

I'm really harmless, so I'm told,
Though I *pretend* to act so bold.

You'll laugh, and think it such great fun
When I decide to take a run;
I run on hind legs, tail in air,
And hope that this will cause a scare.

I hiss and thrash my tail around
To make a really fearsome sound;
And if you're not impressed one bit,
You'll notice that I quickly quit.

I'll run straight up the nearest tree,
(Another chance to laugh at me);

I know when all is said and done
I look so funny when I run.

Even children call me *Frilly,*
Which makes a lizard sound so silly.

I practice hard to earn a name,
To be a dragon of some fame;
But though I try - I never can.
A *lizard* – that is all I am.
But remember I'm a special kind
Of just one species that you'll find;
I'm sometimes called *the forest dweller -*
The lizard with the big umbrella.

THE LLAMA

I look a little like a camel
Just a little (not a lot),
For if you look you'll quickly see
His *hump* I have not got.
I'm intelligent and handsome,
See how gracefully I trot;
Though the camel is my cousin,
He is something I am *not!*

I'm not lazy or bad tempered,
You could never call me 'dim';
It's proven scientifically,
I've a bigger brain than *him!*
I'm a strong but friendly mammal,
Very gentle you will find;
On my back I carry children,
With their luggage packed behind.

I first lived in North America
Thousands of years ago;
That's how I got my woolly coat,
That keeps out cold and snow.
I then migrated to the South,
Because it's warmer there,
Where I wander in the mountains
With the lion and the bear.

My way of talking is to hum,
The sounds I make are many;
But as for vices you could name,
I really haven't *any.*
In fights with friends it's often true
To show whose boss, I'll spit;
I might kick out in self defence,
Or scream a little bit.

But I'm kinder than a camel,
And I know you'll quickly spot
There's not a hump upon *my* back;
It's not a thing I've got!

THE SLENDER LORIS

'I have long slender limbs,' *said the Loris,*
'That's how I was given my name,
And if you should ask about my big eyes,
The reason I have them is plain;
They give me good vision when hunting,
I need to have excellent sight,
How else would I see the small insects
That are visible only at night?'

'In the forests of India you'll find me,'
Said the Loris; 'I live in the trees,
Where I stealthily stalk my unwary prey,
And grab it in both hands with ease.

I'll eat flowers whenever I find them,
And fruit has a taste that's so sweet;
But then there are small birds and reptiles,
That will certainly add to the treat.

I'm the tiniest mammal imagined,
And I sleep in a ball tightly curled;
Did you know that the Loris and Bumble-bee Bat
Are the smallest you'll find in the world?

There's a drug that man has discovered,
Derived from the tears in my eyes;
A remedy used in potions to cure,
A miracle surely to prize;
So you'd think I'd be valued as priceless,
When my eyes hold such precious wee drops;
But still I am critically threatened
Unless deforestation work stops.

My trees are destroyed by the loggers
Who take over most of the land,
Though the Government tries to protect me,
And make local folk understand;
The most they can do is make them aware,
And hope that in future a treasure like me
Will somehow, some day, still be there.'

THE MANATEE

Once long ago, so I am told,
A sailor out at sea,
Cried, *'Look! There swims a mermaid!'*
But he'd never heard of *me*.

They thought me then half human,
But half a *fish* as well,
And that's how mermaids came to be;
Or that's what I've heard tell.

If you'd been at sea for months and months
With not a single break,
You could see how sailors long ago
Could make this small mistake.

For I look just like a lady
Displaying all her charms,
As I swim in shallow water
With my baby in my arms.

Of course my arms are flippers,
(The sailor had poor sight),
But every calf that's born below,
Will swim towards the light.

I'm a large and bulky mammal,
Not handsome there's no doubt,
For my head and face are wrinkled,
And I've whiskers on my snout.

But no creature is more gentle,
And with movements slow and calm
No-one fears a manatee,
He'll never cause you harm.

I'm related to the *elephant*!
This may come as some surprise;
But whereas he must move quite fast,
I need less exercise.

I get my food from sea plants,
And when I come to feed
I lift a flipper to my mouth
To chew each piece of weed.

America is where I live,
Along the coast and bays;
And up and down I slowly graze
The inland waterways.

I'm sometimes called a *sea cow*,
But *he* became extinct
A long way back in history,
Though still our paths are linked.

I've got no natural enemies
Except those known as *man*;
But because I'm so slow moving,
That's how my trials began.

The boats that cruise the shallows
Cause the deaths of manatee,
Who die from injury and shock;
That's why there's less of me.

The legend of the mermaid,
Is romantic you'll agree;
Though we who once inspired the tale,
Might soon be history.

THE MEERKAT

'You're an African mammal that's loved such a lot
For the cute things you do,
and the skill that you've got;
But let's get this right, you don't *look* like a cat,
You're really a mongoose, I'm certain of that.'

*'I'm a mongoose of course. On that we'll agree,
No relation to prairie dogs either,'* said he.

'But why sit so stiffly and stand on two legs?
It seems that a Meerkat just sits there and *begs.*'

*'How stupid you are! Don't you know? Can't you see?
We're on duty as sentries and look-outs,'* said he.

'You're clever, I know, but you've enemies too,
There are eagles and jackals, to name but a few;
Say an eagle attacks as it drops from the sky,
Or a jackal should pounce from a burrow close by.'

'That's why,' said the Meerkat, *'I watch from a tree;
I can call out to warn of the danger I see.'*

'But what if those creatures much bigger than you,
Were met face to face. What then would you do?'

*'Why, we'd all gang together in one angry crowd,
We'd jump, and we'd hiss, and we'd bark very loud;
And we'd growl and we'd spit – as mad as could be!
It works very well for us Meerkats,'* said he.

'But tell me please do, what it is that you *eat*,
When you dig away hard
with those claws on your feet?'

*'I'm looking for eggs from some beetles maybe,
Or roots that are special, or termites,'* said he;
*'I like spiders and worms and the odd snake, it's true,
And I wouldn't say **no** to a scorpion or two.'*

'There's just one more question
that puzzles my brain,
Is it true what I've heard - that you hide from
the *rain?*'

'That's a fact,' the Meerkat replied with a wink,
'It's something I do without stopping to think.
I just hate the rain! When I feel the first drops,
I rush to my burrow - and wait there till it stops!

Now I've answered your questions, and that's quite enough,
Do you think I can waste all my day on such stuff?
I'm starting manoeuvres; I'm due up a tree;
You're blocking my view, sir. So please move!'
said he.

THE STAR-NOSED MOLE

'How most peculiar,' people say,
'Is that his nose, do you suppose?'
And I explain, 'Please - I'm a mole,
And that's the way that my nose grows,
And since it's such a special one,
I follow everywhere it goes.

Mine isn't just a 'smelling' nose,
Mine has tentacles instead;
It's much more sensitive than hands,
It's like a finger that can spread,
And *look* and *feel* for likely food,
Whilst still protruding from my head.

No other creature in the world
Has got a star-shaped nose like mine;
A scientific tracking tool,
Sophisticated, so sublime;
An organ super-sensitive,
Unrivalled since the dawn of time.

Although I'm only sausage-size,
Just watch me dive – and see me swim;
You'll say, *'There goes that famous mole!*
He's like a fish! Just look at him!'
Each foot becomes a paddle then,
Each paddle then becomes a fin.

The wetlands of America
Is somewhere that I'm sure to be;
My winter coat is water-proof,
Cold water doesn't bother me;
And there my nose will feel for fish,
Or worms or insects it can *see*.

Like common moles, I dig and delve,
And make long tunnels underground;
But common moles just don't possess
A nose so perfect, frilled and round;
A nose with feeling so complete,
A nose that with a star is crowned!'

THE MONGOOSE

'Now son,' said the mongoose's father,
'It is time that our story was told:
We can trace our line back to the Pharaohs;
We were buried with all of their gold.
A mongoose was always most honoured
For his services offered to man,
So listen, and then I will tell you
How the stories about us began:

'It is all due to man's interference
In the world's natural order of things,
When they ship goods from country to country,
With no thought of the problems it brings.
In Africa, Asia, and Europe,
The West Indian countries as well,
We were used to effectively rid them of snakes,
And their armies of rats, I've heard tell.

168

'Our employment was like the Pied Piper
Who was hired on an impulse one day
To deliver a town from a huge plague of rats;
And the sum for his trouble: *no pay!*
In *our* case, once the favour was granted,
And no form of thanks had appeared,
We began on their chickens, their pigs and their ducks,
Till the farmers' whole stock disappeared!
It was an island in the West Indies,
Where a notice was nailed to a tree:
Mongooses dead or alive it declared,
And that was how bad things could be.'

'I'm not one for history,' his son said,
(Pretending not to have heard)
'But I'm told we're related to meerkats,
And I find *that* notion absurd.
I was mistaken today for a *weasel*,
And would you believe it - *a cat!*
I'm glad it was just children talking,
I could get very angry at that.'

His father just laughed. 'That's amusing,
They say anger turns one's eyes red;
But keep your anger for special occasions,
Like the battles we're famed for, instead.'

'I'm learning by watching,' his son said,
'It's difficult dealing with snakes.'
And his father replied, 'In the game that *we* play,
You must know there's no room for mistakes.

The skill that you'll need is enormous,
You need to be agile to fight,
And *speed* is of utmost importance;
A young mongoose can die from a bite.'

'But why do you make a snake angry?'
Asked his son; 'It seems senseless to me!'
'That's just a cool trick,' said his father:
'The snake gets exhausted you see.
Our strategy calls for endurance,
To dodge out of reach at each strike;
You must learn how to tumble, to turn and to twist.
No two movements are ever alike.'

'But what if the snake strike is lucky,
Despite all the tricks that you dare?'
'You'll find,' said his father, 'that most of the time
He's just left with a mouthful of *hair!*
And then when at last he's exhausted,
And he stays for a moment quite still,
That's when you dart in and grab him,
Seizing his head for the kill.'

His father went on to convince him,
'A mongoose is nobody's fool,
And our fame has made us a mascot
In many and many a school.'

'I thank you, my father,' his son said,
'For your stories of snake and of man;

But now I am off to wage war on an egg,
And make a good meal if I can.
Do you think that man knows that a mongoose
Is clever at opening eggs?
That we're expert at throwing or hitting them hard
On a rock, while we stand on two legs?'

'He's sure to, my son,' said his father,
'Though *my* tactics are not quite the same:
I lie on my back and, employing four feet,
I just toss them again and again.'

THE BONOBOS MONKEY

We're a link to your prehistory, your evolution too,
So it's not one bit surprising we're the closest ape to you.
Forget about the chimpanzee, so loved and so renowned,
Bonobo 'the forgotten ape' has just been lately found!

We're as close to man, it's reasoned, as a fox is to a dog,
Or just the same relation as a toad is to a frog;
You might find us on the Internet, or see us on TV;
But now of course it's certain that we've just made history.
They called us first just 'pygmy chimps' (they didn't have a clue)
But now we hold the status of a species that is *new*.

We live in isolation in the Congo where we roam,
Unmolested until recently; unrecognized; unknown.
About three million years ago we went our separate way,
And that's why we are different from the chimpanzee today.

We've small heads, narrow shoulders, and our long legs
cause a smile,
It's accepted that, unlike the chimps, bonobos all have style!
We've a flatter, far more open face, enough to make one stare;
And above our lofty forehead there's some neatly parted hair.
We're made more slim and slender and, when we walk or stand,
You'll feel at once you're one of *us*. You'll want to shake our hand!

Chimps are coarse, hot-tempered, and always like to bite;
But we make 'love' instead of war; it's frowned upon to fight.
We are called your 'kissing cousins' as we hug and kiss a lot;
It must be from our breeding this sweet nature that we've got.
Our compassion for each-other is the most amazing sight;
If one of us is blind or deaf we'll make sure they're alright.
We'll pick them up and take them to where they want to go;
We understand if something's wrong. We always seem to know.

One would have thought it possible that, knowing all of this,
The newly found bonobos would be welcomed with a kiss;
And yet our forest now recedes as greedy men intrude,
And even worse - would you believe -
they kill us *just for food!*
Our survival now is jeopardized. It could go either way.
By the time this message reaches you,
we hope that you won't say
'The bonobos just discovered have disappeared today.'

THE HOWLER MONKEY

I'm the noisiest monkey of all of my kind,
The loudest land animal that you will find;
Only the blue whale is louder than me,
And as everyone knows - *his* place is the sea.

You'll hear my loud howling from high in the trees,
Where I whoop and I roar as much as I please:
We males get the blame for all of this noise;
A distinction allotted only to boys.

We howl at the start and the end of each day,
And our voices are heard up to three miles away!
We do it to check out where everyone is;
That our food stays in *our* patch,
our neighbour's in *his*.

Each troop calls to each, so then each takes a turn
To listen for answers; then howls in return.
We sleep quite a lot; fifteen hours every day;
'Good news for your neighbours!' I hear people say.

I've a prehensile tail which is hairy and long,
Like another strong arm to help me hang on.
I eat mostly leaves and I also like fruit;
But I'm large and I'm slow, not pretty or cute.

As half of my forest is no longer there,
I'm sadly endangered and getting quite rare.
But where will you find me? Argentina's one place,
In Mexico, too, you might still see my face.

If you cannot imagine a monkey like me,
Just look at my picture – and then you will see.
Do come to my forest to visit me there;
But if *I* see you first, you will have to take care.

If a large load of fruit falls down 'plop' on your head,
And a howl of loud laughter consumes you with
dread,
Don't turn and run. Just remember, shout *'hi!'*
And you'll know that I'm watching from somewhere
close by.

PYGMY MARMOSET MONKEY
and
PYGMY MOUSE LEMUR

The smallest monkey in the world
Is only *finger* tall;
You might not think a monkey
Could really be that small.
My name is called Marmoset,
But please, if you don't mind,
Write *pygmy* at the front of it,
Or add it on behind.

Find me deep in Ecuador,
Bolivia; Peru;
Or in Brazilian forests,
Where I'll show you what I do:

I will scurry through the branches
With swiftness and with ease,
Where because I am so tiny
I'm well hidden in the trees.
I weigh about five ounces
When I am fully grown;
But since I'm very hard to find,
I'm also little known.

I eat flowers, fruits and berries,
And insects I like too;
But sap from trees I love the best,
I'll chew their bark right through.
With tawny coat streaked through with grey,
And banded yellow-green,
I'm camouflaged so very well
I'm very rarely seen.

The sounds I make are many,
It's important how I 'speak',
For there's lots of different signals
In a whistle, trill, or squeak.
And there are noises that I make,
Heard only by *my* ear,
Of such high pitch which humans
Could never hope to hear.
Though I'm the smallest monkey,
It's important to announce
The smallest primate in the world
Weighs only just *one ounce!*

He lives in Madagascar,
An island in the sea
Just off the coast of Africa,
Thousands of miles from me.

A lemur most extraordinary,
He well deserves his fame,
He's called a Pygmy Mouse Lemur;
Please don't forget his name.
He would fit inside an egg shell,
(A chicken's egg, that is),
He's called a *mouse* lemur because
That's just the size he is.

But our freedom days are numbered,
We're disappearing fast;
It's a matter of conjecture
How much longer we can last.
If only those most powerful -
The mighty human race,
Would think of precious mites like us
And leave a little space.

We're both of us endangered,
Because, as you might guess,
We're losing all our natural trees;
And death is caused by stress.
Imagine if you will, our plight,
Then think of all the fuss
If *humans* had to fight for life –
And then please think of *us.*

THE SNEEZING MONKEY

High in the mountains of Burma I am,
You'd believe I was safe from the clutches of man;
Yet hunters surround me, with loggers below,
And there's simply no place for a monkey to go.
I'm in danger so great in my rainforest tree
That there's only a few of us left, that's like me.

And the great pity is that I'm really unique,
Just look, if you can, at my face and physique:
I'm big, with black fur, with white tufts on each ear,
And you'll see my pink face if I let you come near;
I've a fluffy moustache with a matching white beard,
But just look at my nose: You'll say *'isn't that weird!'*

It isn't *a nose* – it's just two little slits
That would surely drive anyone out of their wits;
It's no good at all where I live, in the rain,
In fact the whole problem could drive me insane.

I sit with my head tucked up to my knees,
And I snuffle and sneeze – and I *sneeze* – and I
sneeze!

I just hate the wet when it gets up my nose,
And the trouble it gives me – well, nobody knows!
So I envy all those with a nose that is thin;
Or long; that points down, so the rain can't get in.
I wouldn't much care if it grew big or small,
But it's really so sad not to have one at all!

The first drops of rain always fill me with dread,
As I sit on a branch with a leaf on my head;
And all I can do is to anxiously wait
For the powers that be, to decide on my fate.
There's nowhere to hide. I think you'll agree,
The moment I sneeze, people know where I'll be!

But there's one fact I feel I must certainly add,
That you may not yet know, that's as sad as it's bad:
Those who discover such creatures as me,
Are not those professors who come purposely,
But loggers or miners; those digging the soil
In the hope of quick profits - like drilling for oil.

In my case, I was noticed because of those crews,
And then I got published and made the world news!
That meant I was famous as more people came
To see the strange monkey who sneezed in the rain.
Just think (if I'm lucky and left to roam free)
The world might not lose such a monkey as me!

THE MOOSE

Please don't call a moose - *a mouse,*
It's really such a shame
To get my name so muddled up.
Please listen, I'll explain:

Though *moose* and *mouse* sound similar,
We're not alike at all,
You couldn't miss a mighty moose;
I'm not exactly *small.*
I've got big ears, a droopy nose,
And underneath my chin
There dangles - like a little bell -
A fur flap long and thin.

I'm like a deer, but bigger,
With a rather humpy back;
And every male has antlers
Like a crown set on a rack.

You might ask, *'Why grow antlers?'*
But think, if they weren't there,
How would I face a pack of wolves?
Or fight a fierce bear?
A moose cannot escape of course,
If he gets stuck in snow;
He's much too big and clumsy,
And there's just nowhere to go.

Canada is where I live,
And in Alaska, too;
And if you listen carefully,
I'll tell you what I do:

I live in woods and marshy land,
And in the winter snow
I paw and search for grass and twigs
That's buried there below.
In water I will often wade
To forage and to feed,
And stick my head deep underneath
To search for water weed.

A moose is strange to look at,
As I've mentioned once before;
And with my top lip hanging down,
I seem all chin and jaw.

But moose are brilliant swimmers,
And oh, how I can run!
There's lots of things I'm famous for,
I've only just begun.

A moose is big and beautiful,
A truly wondrous thing,
And in the forest where I live,
The people call me King.
'There goes the mighty moose!' they say,
'He's very famous here;
You'll know him when you see him,
He's much bigger than a deer.'

THE OCELOT

There is no creature living
That has a coat like mine;
Golden fur splashed over
With patterns so divine;
Necklaces of chains and circles,
Rings and ribbons; lines and links;
Black and brown and tawny tan,
Like drawings made with pen and ink.

Through the forest corridors
I pass from light to shade,
And hiding in the brushwood
My painted colours fade;
With amber eyes ablaze I steal
Between tall grasses blended in;
And like a ghost I shift and change,
To pass and vanish deep within.

But sadly I'm endangered,
And to a high degree;
Although there's few such creatures
As beautiful as me.
And yet I'm starved of territory,
I'm hunted for a pet;
My fur is still much coveted;
I'm always under threat.

I come from South America,
From Mexico; Peru;
And though I hunt in grassland,
I hunt in tree-tops too.
I'm a small nocturnal creature
That mostly hunts at night,
And, like all cats, my special eyes
Reflect to catch the light.

I'm a solitary stalker,
Once worshipped long ago;
A cat with expert swimming skills
Of which few people know.
I ask, what small cat living,
Still wild and running free,
Deserves to be protected
More urgently than me?

THE OKAPI

If you thought I was a zebra,
Then of course you would be wrong;
And you might mistake me for giraffe,
Because my neck is long;
I don't know why I'm made this way,
Or how I came to be;
The reason why I'm half and half,
Is quite a mystery.

I've got just one relation
Whose neck has brought him fame;
It's quite the longest in the world,
So you might guess his name.

I'm thinking of giraffe of course;
He looks a bit like me,
But as I'm nowhere near his size,
You might well disagree.

Giraffe can use his mighty neck
To reach the highest tree,
And so he spies a long way off
A likely enemy;
But I don't need to browse too high,
When plodding on my way;
I relish plants much lower down
To forage every day.

I've stripes upon my back legs,
And more upon my rump;
And just the sudden sight of me
Might easily make you jump.
But they are just my camouflage,
To hide me through the trees,
And to tell our young Okapis,
'This way! Follow please!'

I live far off in Africa,
I'm secretive and shy;
And if you've never heard of me,
Well that's the reason why.
You'd never guess I've got a tongue
That's coloured black and blue;
You'd never guess the length of it,
Or the things that it can do.

I wrap it round the leaves of trees,
I grasp; I pull; I clutch;
Only giraffe, and me of course,
Have tongues that do so much.
How many others do you know
That use their tongues to clean
Their ears, and then their eye-lids,
And all the bits between?

My ears are very big, because
I must be quick to hear
The sounds of any leopards;
Those creatures I most fear.
I hide when it is daylight,
Where the undergrowth is dense,
And feed on higher ground at night,
Which always makes good sense.

Most mammals out of Africa,
(Whose names you're sure to know)
Were discovered by zoologists
A long, long time ago;
But because I was so secretive,
And hid myself so well,
There was no-one who could see me,
And so nobody could *tell*.

But now that I'm discovered,
I'm endangered tragically
By the logging of my forest
And by those who covet me.

I'm relished by the hunters,
Who, filled with greed, don't care
That I'm a 'listed animal'
Remarkable and rare.

But to those who've grown to love me,
With no thought of greed or gain;
I say to those, 'Remember me -
Okapi is my name!'

THE OPOSSUM

I shared the land with dinosaurs,
I think that you should know,
And though of course they're now extinct,
I'm still around, and so
I think I'm rather special,
Just like the kangaroo,
One of my rare relations
Of which there are but few.

I'm *not* related to the rat,
I *don't* hang upside-down;
They're just facts that you might get wrong
Which make opossums frown.

I have a secret pouch, you know,
Just like the kangaroo,
To carry new-born babies in;
The koala has one, too.
And when my pouch is feeling full,
And it's too tight inside,
The babies climb upon my back,
So they can have a ride.

'Playing possum' is a game
I play when I'm alarmed;
I lie quite still, as if I'm dead,
And hope I'll not be harmed.
Whoever then attacks may think
'This is no fun for me,'
And hopefully they'll turn away,
And leave me to run free.

That's clever of me, isn't it?
But that's not *all* I do;
I'll hiss - and show my fifty teeth.
(They're fifty sharp ones too.)
I've more teeth than any mammal
That lives upon the land;
And my tail is quite prehensile;
I can use it like a hand.
It's useful too, for balancing,
And to cling above my head;
But I don't hang upside-down by it,
As I've already said.

I eat all kinds of insect things,
But please don't think me rude
If you should find me crunching snails,
(These are my favourite food);
And a cockroach or a cricket
Are tasty with slug sauce;
Whilst beetles on the menu
Make a scrumptious second course.

I'm no bigger than a house cat,
(Or that's what I've heard tell)
And I'm found throughout America,
And Canada as well.
I'm really shy and secretive,
But should we chance to meet,
You'll say, *'How quite adorable!*
Oh, aren't opossums sweet!'

THE ORANG-UTAN

From Borneo our homeland,
Please hear our desperate call,
From the world's most ancient forest,
The last frontier of all.
Our forests are the richest,
Most priceless found on earth,
The source of untapped treasures
Of unimagined worth;
A storehouse filled with remedies
For ills of every kind;
Herbs and roots, and bark from trees,
To benefit mankind.

And here we've lived for centuries,
Almost since Time began,
Unique amongst the few great apes
That still are known to man.
The Old Men of the Forest
The natives called us here,
And as they left us quite alone,
Of them we had no fear.

But men now come here every day,
Who kill Orang-utans;
Those men so blinded with their greed –
The dreaded chain-saw gangs.
Their logging trails are all around,
Vast tracks of land lie bare;
We look in vain for where to hide –
But where? we ask; *but where?*

Impatient with the time it takes
To cut with just a saw,
They burn great swathes of forestry
With no regard for law.
Huge canopies of green are lost
As more and more they clear;
Yet the life of all the planet,
The breath of life is here.

Mothers with their babies cling,
And look towards the sky,
As if *someone – somewhere* up there
Must hear their piteous cry.

They climb in terror upwards
And watch with painful breath
As the flames creep ever closer,
And they turn to meet their death.

But we know there's some amongst you
Who will help us if they can;
Those wise brave-hearted saviours,
Who are surely known to man.
They tell the world about our plight,
They ask the question *Why?*
For once our world of trees is gone,
Man's world will also die.

THE OSTRICH

I'll understand if you don't like me,
I don't see why you should;
For I know that I'm not pretty,
And I'm very seldom good.

My neck looks quite atrocious,
Just a huge expanse of skin
That hovers there above me,
Like a serpent long and thin.
My legs are quite extraordinary,
I stand at eight foot high;
And with my silly fluffy wings,
Of course I cannot fly.

My feet look like a dinosaur's,
I've two large knobbly toes,
And on the front are big strong claws;
You must beware of those!

If I was nice, a *friendly* bird,
It wouldn't be so bad,
You might forget about my looks
And maybe still be glad.
But an ostrich is the biggest
And the strongest bird alive;
Stand too close and you'll get nipped
Before you count to five!
You can't out-run an ostrich
If you should make one cross;
I'll chase you and I'll kick you
To show you who's the boss!
You ask what kind of noise I make,
I'll tell you, I can *roar!*
But usually I loudly *hiss*;
You can't call *me* a bore.

I expect you've heard the tale somewhere,
So silly that it's sad,
"An ostrich hides his head in holes"
Do people think we're mad?
My eyes with their long lashes
Are beady but they're bright,
And I can see you *miles* away,
I have such marvellous sight.
At the first real sign of danger

I'd simply streak right past;
I'd be caught for speeding on the road
Because I run so fast.

'At forty miles an hour, young sir,
I'll have to take you in!'
But a policeman couldn't catch me,
And so of course I'd win!
I'm the fastest runner in the world
That runs on legs of *two*;
Have you seen the length of them?
That should give some clue.

So though you may not like me much,
I've great pride in myself;
And there are things an ostrich has,
That some would count as wealth.

No feathers are more beautiful
Than from my tail and wings;
They're used for fans, and ladies' hats,
And highly prized by kings.
My eggs are always treasured, too;
I'm sure you must have heard,
An ostrich has the biggest egg
That's laid by *any* bird.

In Africa you'll find me,
Where I roam both far and wide;
And if you feel you're brave enough
Jump up and take a ride!

THE RIVER OTTER

You'll hardly ever see me,
For I'm secretive and shy;
There's just a snaking bubble trail
To show where I've passed by.
I live along the river bank
By shores of lakes or streams,
And anyone who's searched for me
Will know how hard it seems.
First you'll see a nose appear,
Then two dark shining eyes,
And a brown face full of whiskers
From the water will arise.

We're built for speed and that is why
All otters have webbed feet;
Our large tails help to give us thrust,
Which makes us hard to beat.

We swim as smoothly as an eel,
We somersault with ease;
We twist and turn and roll about,
Whichever way we please.
We all have streamlined bodies
Of extraordinary grace;
And if we wish to disappear,
We can, without a trace.

Don't mistake us for our cousin,
The otter from the sea;
For though we both *look* much alike,
We do things differently.
He always swims with belly *up,*
His fur is full of air,
While we swim with our bellies *down;*
It's easy to compare.

We'll often eat when basking
On the river where we laze,
And float out with the current
With our tummies as our trays.
We'll tumble like an acrobat,
Clap hands with furry paws,
And do all kinds of clever tricks
That everyone adores.

That's why to every audience
We're such a rare delight;
We hope you'll catch a glimpse of us.
If you're lucky - you just might!

THE GIANT PANDA

Everybody loves me,
And to help you guess my name
Just think of one enchanting bear
Of quite outstanding fame.

In China where I come from,
I'm called *a big bear cat,*
And with my rather cat-like eyes
I look a bit like that.
My pupils are just little slits,
Whilst other bears' are round;
And that's just one surprising thing
Of many that they've found.

I'm really very different
From other bears you'll see;
My front paws have five fingers,
Which is odd, you must agree;
I've also got a kind of thumb
To hold my food to eat,
Which I must admit is useful,
And it does look rather neat.

I live high in the mountains,
Where it's cloudy, cool, and wet;
And there I sit and eat my food
(The little I can get),
For all I eat are bamboo shoots,
And that is very sad,
For what is to become of me,
When there's no more to be had?

I swim, as well as climb a tree,
And I'll tell you something more:
I never stand on *my* hind legs
Like other bears - and *roar.*
I'll make no noise to frighten you,
I'm never fierce; I'm shy.
And I never *ever* hibernate;
I don't eat enough, that's why.

My country's gift of peace I am,
A most familiar sight:
A kindly, cuddly giant bear,
All coloured black and white.
When people ask, *'Who's loved the most?*
'The rarest mammal, who is he?'
I have to answer truthfully,
'Without a doubt - *that's me!'*

THE GIANT PANGOLIN

I look rather like a pinecone
When I roll into a ball,
For I'm very brown and scaly,
But you wouldn't call me *small*.
My tongue is not small either,
It's the longest you will find;
The same size as my scaly tail
That follows me behind.

I'm like the scaly monsters
Who evolved long years ago;
And I'm rather like the Ant-Eater,
A creature you might know.
Of course he isn't scaly,
Though he eats ants just like me,
But we're both ferocious 'diggers',
And we both *don't* climb a tree.

My claws are so enormous
That, as you might have heard,
They affect my way of walking,
Which most people find absurd;
So I walk upon my knuckles
In a posture that is new;
Since with this disability
It's the best that I can do.

When threatened I will play this trick:
I quickly turn and *roll,*
It's so much quicker, don't you think,
Than to run and find a hole?
I can curl myself so tightly
That no human hand, I'm told,
Can tug or prise me open,
And force me to unfold.

My eyes have two thick eyelids,
I can close my ears and nose;
(Which is useful when the ants sting,
It protects me from all those.)
And Pangolins can also swim,
So with my sense of smell,
(And the other things I've mentioned)
I think I do quite well.

In Africa or Asia,
You will find me I am sure;
I'll be sniffing round the tree roots,
Since my eyesight is so poor.
That's why I move quite slowly,
Since it's difficult to *see,*
But I'm never ever frightened,
For my mother said to me:

"Your armour will protect you,
Whoever you might meet;
Survival mostly goes with those
Most difficult to eat!"

THE GREAT WHITE PELICAN

When you think of a bird that's as strange as can be,
Who's fantastic and funny - that bird must be *me*.
I'm one of the biggest, the best of my kind,
With the longest beak, too, of any you'll find.
And though I am normally feathered in *white*,
When breeding time comes I go *pink* with delight.

If you want to know countries to find where I am,
There's Africa, Asia, from Greece to Vietnam.
Of course I'm most famous because of my beak;
It's the subject about which most people will speak.
I fill it with water in huge gulps - then drain,
And once I have done it, I do it again.

I'll swallow whole-heartedly all the trapped fish,
Or keep them for later, if that's what I wish;
I've a pouch where I keep them; a bag when I 'shop',
Where they'll stay till I'm ready and where they can stop.
But sometimes we pelicans all form a line,
And we fish in a group - which I think is divine;
Then we chase schools of fish into shallows or pools,
And scoop them all up, using beaks for our tools.

My nest is quite frightful! A mess, I admit;
But as I'm not house-proud I don't care one bit.
I'm not tidy or careful. Those branches I pick
Can be any old rubbish - like leaves or a stick.
But you ask if I *swim?* And I have to confess,
I don't like my feathers to get in a mess.
I'm too big and heavy for swimming you see,
And even on land I look odd, you'll agree.

But with flying it's different. I'll fly with no stop
For three hundred miles! That's quite a long hop.
I'll fly all day long and all the night too,
It takes quite some doing, if only you knew.
Like a heron I soar, and we both have this knack
Of gracefully gliding with head held way back.

People say that I'm quite an inquisitive bird,
As well as quite quarrelsome; that's what I've heard.
But really a pelican never is rude,
He just likes to know *who* is queuing for food.
And he wants a few answers to *why* someone's there;
And *what* he is doing, and *who's* standing *where.*

Remember my name; I'm called *the Great White*,
Since my wings are the biggest. There's no grander sight.
But I'll argue and squabble (like pelicans do)
On the *Why* and the *Where*, and the *How* and the *Who.*

THE EMPEROR PENGUIN

I know that I'm a funny bird,
And here's the reason why:
I have to waddle as I walk,
Because I cannot fly.
Once we penguins all had wings,
But that was long ago;
Now they're used as flippers,
For swimming, or to row.

I can swim both fast and deep
In my pursuit of fish;
For underneath the water
This is my favourite dish.
I use my tail for steering,
I brake with both my feet;
In water I can almost fly,
My act is hard to beat.

My coat of feathers black and white,
Is like a little suit;
I'm everybody's favourite
Because I look so cute;
And I have cousins far away
Who don't live in the snow;
The islands where they live are warm,
I think that you should know.
As the biggest of the penguins,
I'm an Emperor by name;
And I perform one mighty act
That gives me claim to fame.
When mother lays her penguin egg,
I keep it from the cold;
I push it gently with my beak
Till on my feet it's rolled.

I hold it balanced there with care,
My feathers keep it warm,
And there I stand for days and nights,
Through wintry snow and storm;
In all that time I do not eat,
Nor any comfort take,
But stay on guard for weeks and weeks,
All for that dear egg's sake.

I know it's quite incredulous,
In fact it's quite absurd;
I feel that I'm an animal,
And only *half* a bird.

But if you don't believe the things
I've told you that I do,
You'll have to read some penguin books,
And then you'll know they're true.

Whatever way you look at it,
I think you must agree,
Amongst the birds that do *not* fly,
You can't improve on **me**!

THE DUCK BILLED PLATYPUS

I'm quite the oddest animal
That you will ever see:
What other mammal in the world
Can lay an egg like me?

The answer might surprise you,
If you haven't got a clue;
It's my dear old friend Echidna -
And between us we make *two*.
But Echidna looks quite different,
He's not like me at all;
He looks just like a hedgehog,
A big and prickly ball.

I'm sometimes nicknamed *water-mole,*
I got that name it seems
Because I burrow with my claws,
And yet I swim in streams.

You might mistake me for a *fish*,
But that's how I can tease;
I look half reptile, half a bird,
But *no* - I'm none of these!
I've a tail that's like a beaver's,
A big wide duck-like beak,
I've front feet like a mole to dig;
No wonder I'm a freak!
You'd hardly think with my webbed feet
I'd burrow on the land;
But when my claws withdraw their web,
Hey, look! I've got *a hand.*
And when I'm swimming deep in pools
Another thing I do
Is purposely close both my eyes;
This, too, might puzzle you.

How does he look for food? you ask.
I simply use my beak;
It's soft and flexible, you see,
To touch; to feel; to seek.
I find all sorts of things to eat,
Like shrimps and eggs of fish,
And a frog or two adds flavour
To any kind of dish.

My coat is shiny, soft as silk,
And envied very much;
It's extra warm, two layers thick,
Like velvet to the touch.
I've very few real enemies,

A snake or two maybe;
Or sometimes there's a water rat,
Or fox that threatens me.

In Australia and Tasmania
I'm now well recognized;
They think that I'm a miracle,
And here I'm highly prized.
You'll find my picture everywhere
(Just like the kangaroo)
And I'm very well protected
By people just like you.

It took the experts by surprise
When they discovered *me*,
And even now they've found few clues
As to my ancestry.
"A mammal hatched out from an egg!
How did this come to be?"

It will take another billion years
To find another *me,*
And by the time they've solved my case
By some peculiar means,
I might have disappeared from view
And be just the stuff of dreams.

THE NEW WORLD PORCUPINE

In two main regions of the world
Our population grew,
So the scientists have grouped us
In the Old World and the New.
I'm the New World porcupine,
Whose home is in a tree,
Quite different from the other kind,
As you will shortly see.

You'll never meet a better clown
Wherever you might go,
So I'm requesting urgently,
Do come and watch my show:
See me wobble my bulbous nose
And wave my fat little paws,
As I dizzily hang from a tree branch
By my tail instead of my claws.

You might not actually *see* me
From my perch high up in the trees,
For I often look like a bird's nest,
I'm such a terrible tease.
Sometimes I'll venture down for a swim,
Sometimes I'll whine or wail;
I can change my voice to a cough or shriek,
As I hang by my hairy tail.

But when I drop to the world below,
And feel my feet on the ground,
That's when you'll get the chance to see
A porcupine clowning around.
Of course I *know* that I'm funny,
I know that I'm playing for laughs,
So I clown away in my own sweet way,
Whilst you take your photographs.

Of monkeys it's said "they're quite human"
Which always raises a smile,
And some creatures are comic to look at,
That you see just once in a while;
But porcupines really are different,
So take some advice from me,
To watch two having a boxing match
Is the funniest sight you'll see.

One never touches the other chap,
That's one of the rules of the game;
And our manners are always friendly,
There's never a question of blame.

I just bunch up my little front paws,
Sway dizzily to and fro,
About to go down for the count it seems,
After the knock-out blow.
But the game can end as soon as it starts
If one of us gets an 'itch',
The contestant stops for a blissful scratch,
Then rolls off into a ditch.

I can act incredibly stupid
With such disarming good grace,
You'll laugh as well as feel sorry,
At the sight of my puzzled face.
*'You stumbling kindly creature,
You're a fool - from your eyes to your toes,'*
But that's all part of my comical act;
The comedy grows and grows.

Just watch me juggle a mango,
And see where my antics lead,
As I fumble and clumsily stumble
Always more than I actually need.
You'll think I have dropped it for certain,
But look what an expert can do;
No clown in a circus can match me,
It's quite obvious *who* could train *who.*

I know I'm a comical creature,
But that's why you'll love me for sure;
And once you have seen me performing,
You'll always be wishing for more.

THE OLD WORLD PORCUPINE

You couldn't call me beautiful,
You can't admire a spine,
But I've *thirty-thousand* of them,
And all of them are mine.

So it's really not important
That my movements are so slow,
For I'm very well respected
In whatever place I go;
And it's really not important
That my eyesight is so poor,
For my sense of smell is excellent,
So who could ask for more?

My hearing, too, is very good,
And since I like to roam,
I've forests, deserts, grasslands,
In which to make my home.

I'm always well identified
From tip of nose to toe,
Through Canada, America,
And on to Mexico.

In two main regions of the world
Our population grew,
So the scientists have grouped us
In the Old World and the New.
I'm the Old World porcupine,
Who lives upon the ground,
In caves or rocks or burrows,
That I have dug or found.

When I'm feeling calm and friendly,
All my spines will lie down flat;
A sure sign that I like you,
You can quite depend on that.
But whenever I feel threatened,
All my spines begin to rise,
And then I'll turn my back to you,
And do this exercise:

I'll tuck my head between my legs,
Approach you from the rear,
And hope that such a prickly sight
Will fill your heart with fear;
Then, if you take no notice,
I will rattle with my tail,
And stamp my feet in anger;
And if *this* trick should fail,

I'll just run backwards into you
My own peculiar way,
To spear you with my many spikes,
And some may stick and *stay*.

Of course I soon grow new ones
If I leave the old with you,
And though my spikes aren't poisonous,
They're painful, it is true.
Despite a body full of spines,
I wear soft underwear;
Warm wool grows round my belly parts,
To keep me comfy there.

I chew all kinds of funny things:
Bones; leather; antlers; wood;
And plants and bark of trees I eat,
Because they do me good.
I'm not a bit aggressive,
(Though not cuddly, I agree),
But if you treat me kindly,
You could make a friend of me.

THE BRUSHTAIL POSSUM

Because of population growth,
I've no home, it is said;
And that's why (being clever)
I'll make *yours* mine instead.

I'm a possum with a difference,
And with my trusty crew
I live round people's houses,
So I'll share some space with you,
And act as an inspector
To check your house all through.

Your house might be in disrepair,
Or if work's left undone
That's when *I* shall pay a call,
And I'll have lots of fun
Between the ceilings and the floors,
Where I can jump and run.

You'll hear me thumping on your roof,
Or calling to my mate,
And I'll laugh at the disruption
When your house is in a state;
It will take what seems forever
To put my mischief straight.

I might fall down your chimney,
Or pop up through your floor,
But please don't try to catch me,
For I've claws on every paw;
Just use some wise persuasion
And entice me through the door.

I'm a native of Australia,
Where I'm treated as a guest;
But over in New Zealand
I'm considered just a pest.
It's a pity, since a possum
Always treats life with such zest.

I've nice long ears, a bushy tail,
I'm coloured silver-grey;
And you'll find me up a gum tree,
Where I sleep throughout the day;
But when dark comes my awful screams
Might frighten you away!

I'm like a little fox or cat,
A cute and furry friend;

With a possum pouch for joeys,
That I with love will tend;
So please look on me kindly,
As I've no wish to offend.

I'm supposed to be protected
As all of you should know;
But because I am so naughty
My tale is one of woe,
And I have to make an exit
As fast as I can go!

THE SPOTTED-TAILED QUOLL

Have you seen my spotted tail?
There's nothing wrong with *that;*
I look rather like a possum,
A little like a cat;
But I'm also called *a tiger quoll*,
And *tiger cat* as well;
And since the thought occurred to me,
I feel that I must tell:

It's a *leopard* not a *tiger*
(I'm sure without a doubt)
That wears my spots upon his coat,
Not the other way about.
So why then call me *tiger*
When there's not one stripe I've got?
Someone, somewhere, got it wrong,
Or else they just forgot.

I've not just got a spotted *tail,*
As far as I can see
My spots continue down my back,
(They're all a part of me).
But if people only see my tail
When I'm halfway up a tree,
There must be lots of silly ones
Who think that's *all* of me!

Australia is my homeland,
At least I know *that's* right;
But you'll be lucky if you meet me,
As I only hunt at night.
I'm a carnivorous marsupial,
A little hard to say;
Carnivorous means that I eat meat,
It just describes my prey.

And marsupials all have pouches
For carrying their young;
A pocket hidden out of sight,
Somewhere securely hung.
You'll think me very handsome
If we meet, without a doubt.
'Look! Isn't that a Spotted Quoll?'
'How splendid!' you will shout.

Did you know that quolls are famous?
When Captain Cook first came,
He collected us along the coast,
And then wrote down our name.

Our name is aboriginal,
That's how it came to us;
But as the *biggest* quoll with spots,
I get a lot more fuss.

There's a cause called 'Quolls in Danger',
But of course you might not know
Of baiting; land loss; foxes; cats;
That threaten us, and so
There are groups that try to help us,
Who try to show they care;
So that one day in the future
A quoll might still be there!

THE RACCOON

I live mostly in America,
But also Mexico;
And Canada is another place
I live, that you might know.
My name means *One who washes,*
And as food is such a treat,
I always wash with water
All my food before I eat.
It's really just a habit,
But a good one you'll agree;
There's no mammal I can think of
Who does the same as me.

I'm little brother to the bear,
And from the Indian race
I got the name of *Magic One* -
The One with painted face.

I'm also called *a bandit*,
Because of my disguise;
You'll see the small black mask I wear
That covers both my eyes.
My bushy tail is patterned, too,
With four or more black rings;
And since my paws have five toes each,
They're used for lots of things.
My quick and clever fingers
Are as nimble as they're long;
As clever as the sly raccoon
To whom they all belong!

I get on well with humans,
I'll make your home my own;
But my visits will be nightly,
And I'll always come alone.
I'm a proper kind of bandit,
I will raid and steal your stores;
Since with my nimble fingers
I can lift the latch on doors.
I've learnt to open boxes,
I can get in rubbish bins;
But this is just a very few
Amongst my *many* sins.

I'll hide inside your chimneys,
Or in your attic space;
I'll dig up all your garden;
I'm always in disgrace.
Can't keep me out with fences,
A fence will never do;
I'll get *under* them or *over* them,
Or simply scramble *through*.

One thing you'll find for certain,
Although I'm rarely seen
I'll leave my tracks on everything
To show you where I've been.
Each hand and footprint that you find
You're sure to think is fun;
For each looks like a human hand,
A tiny baby one.

Few creatures do what I can do:
Run headfirst down a tree;
My hind-foot rotates right around,
From back to front, you see.
With my short legs and my flat feet,
I waddle on the ground,
And as I store a lot of fat,
My body gets quite round.
In winter I may sleep for weeks
In quite a dozy state,
But in-between I go for walks;
I never hibernate.

I get in lots of trouble,
I'm a nuisance it is true;
My little hands get everywhere,
When I find something new.
To lots of folk I'm just a pest,
But don't you think that's sad?
I'm sure with my intelligence
Not *all* of me is bad.
I'm not on the endangered list,
On this we can agree;
But always lock your door at night -
There's lots around like me!

THE CLOUD RAT

As soon as anyone mentions *rats* -
You can guarantee without fail
That people will gasp and shake their heads,
Whilst turning a shade more pale.
But don't be misled; there are rats – and rats –
Not all of them true to their name;
There are creatures not really like rats at all,
They just *look* a little the same.

But amongst a rat's many relations,
There is someone quite special – like me;
I come from the Philippine Islands
Just off the South China Sea.
My name is the Bushy Tailed Cloud Rat,
And you might ask the question, *but why*?
It's because I live high in the mountains,
Close to the clouds and the sky.

I've large feet adapted for clinging,
For climbing each tall forest tree,
But I'm active only at night-time;
A solitary soul – that is me.
To look at, I'm perfectly gorgeous,
With a tail quite incredibly long;
But sadly my forest gets smaller each day,
I'm endangered and soon might be gone.

It seems I'm a good form of protein
For most local people to eat;
And my thick cosy fur makes warm winter hats,
Much admired, and considered a treat.
I'm a rare and a beautiful creature,
Though I'm hunted the same for all that;
But think - *I'm the biggest rat in the world* -
A rat that's as big as a CAT!

THE RHINOCEROS

I'm ugly; I'm big; I'm a monster;
But *dinosau*r isn't my name,
Although I look very much like one,
A Rhino' is not quite the same.

Its millions of years since I came here,
Sixty to be quite precise;
Just think what a lot of relations!
To meet some I think would be nice.

I've elephants' feet which look funny,
My hair is like buffalo hair;
I've a horn like a unicorn! *Isn't that grand?*
No wonder you all come to stare.

A *Rhinoceros* – that's what they call me:
My name means *a nose with a horn*,
If it looks most ferocious, I'm sorry,
But that's just the way I was born.

Rhino's are usually friendly,
Though we do look so scary and big;
And although our horn is for fighting,
We do sometimes use it to *dig*.

My ears swivel round to hear noises,
I snort, and I honk, and I roar!
But some spectacles would come in handy,
As my eye-sight I know is quite poor.

I have to move my head sideways
To help me to see straight ahead,
So I never rely just on 'seeing',
I *hear* and *smell* danger instead.

I'll charge at you if I get frightened,
(Though I'm big, I haven't much brain),
And I'll move at a most astonishing speed -
I can rumble along like a train.

But what creature on land is the biggest?
I'll surprise you. It isn't *quite* me,
But I'm *next* in the world to the biggest;
An elephant's bigger than me!

THE SAKIWINKI MONKEY

You might think my name
Sounds a bit like a game;
It's not very easy to say it.
If it muddles your head,
Call me *Saki* instead;
I think that I really prefer it.

In my green forest towers
I eat fruit, I eat flowers,
I'm a monkey of squirrel proportions;
But my little black face
Is not easy to trace,
As I'm visible only in portions.

My twittering cries
Might cause you surprise,
As I rarely come down to the ground;
If you ask how I drink,
And you really can't think,
The answer is simple I've found.

If you think of the rain,
It's not hard to explain
How useful my tree house can be;
It fulfils every wish,

When each leaf makes a dish;
A convenience especially for me.

But my *tongue* I don't use,
For that's not how I choose
To drink when water's close by;
My hands become tools,
That I soak in the pools,
And I then lick them perfectly dry.

Look well when we meet,
At my arms, hands, and feet,
You might catch a glimpse as I jump;
There's a bright orange tint,
And there's also a hint
Of green on my shoulders and rump.

I've a mask round my face
That's in just the right place,
And the hair on my big ears is white;
I look like a flower
In my green leafy tower;
I'm a monkey that's sure to delight!

But I think it's a shame
When I'm trained to be tame;
A *Saki* should live his life free.
So please leave me alone
When you visit my home;
I'm better off here - in a tree!

The little Sakiwinki monkey lives in the Guyana rainforest of South America.

THE ELEPHANT SEAL

Because of my peculiar nose,
I may not look quite real;
You might not quite believe me
When I tell you I'm a seal.
I'm the biggest of my species
With this very special nose;
It's fashioned rather like a trunk,
It's funny how it grows.
It's not long, like an elephant's,
But it's one of which I'm proud;
As well as holding water,
It helps me roar quite loud!
No other mammal holds their breath
Under water quite like me,
Or dives to such amazing depths
To hunt for food at sea.

In all the world's great oceans
Two types of me appear,
And they are in the Northern
And the Southern hemisphere.
In the North Pacific Ocean
All the Northern seals will be;
But it's South of the Antarctic
Where you'll find seals like *me.*
An octopus, a welcome catch,
Adds relish to my meals;
And then a little shark or two,
Goes well with squid and eels.
I spend my time digesting
All my food beneath the deep;
And though I sometimes take a nap,
I never *ever* sleep.

I feed where other predators
Could never even *see,*
In almost total darkness;
But they don't have eyes like *me.*
You simply would not comprehend
The depths to which I dive;
No mammal would attempt it,
They'd be quickly crushed alive!

Yet seals are classed as mammals,
And this just goes to show
How very special are the seals
Who go where *I* will go.

We once were hunted mercilessly,
Like every ocean whale;
The hunt was for our blubber
On a simply massive scale.

Extinction stared us in the face
In almost every land;
But thanks to present strict controls,
Most hunting now is banned;
And all those curious visitors
Who see us on a beach,
Stand quite transfixed with wonder,
Sometimes devoid of speech.

"Just look at all those giant slugs,
With thick grey wrinkled skins,
Like aliens with their trunk-like nose,
Each with tails and fins!"

To which I think I should reply,
'I warn you, please take heed,
A bull seal can attack you
With most surprising speed!
We might *look* both fat and lazy,
But we're neither slow nor weak;
And seals with noses just like ours,
Are considered quite unique.'

THE HARP SEAL

I come from the cold North Atlantic,
Where I spend lots of time out at sea;
But from the Arctic, from Russia to Greenland,
It's all the same shore-line to me.

In Norway they call me 'a sea dog',
The French call me 'wolf of the sea',
But I'm commonly known as *a harp seal*
Because of the pattern on me.
It's a shape like a harp or a horseshoe,
A band of irregular black;
You'll see what I mean when you meet me,
You'll say, *'there's the harp on his back.'*

If you watch a seal when he's swimming
You might be surprised when you find
That his front flippers never propel him,
He uses those only behind.

He's also got excellent eyesight,
Most useful when one is a seal,
For in dimly lit, deep Arctic waters,
One could easily end up as a meal!

We seals swim in big groups together,
We all dive and leap in one go,
And we move really fast if we have to,
Across the packed ice of a floe.
We might meet a polar bear hunting,
(Who we'll always avoid if we can)
Or we might bump into a walrus
Or meet our old enemy, *man.*

There are sharks and whales in the water,
The world is a perilous place;
But the fate that is kept for our babies,
Is the worst that *any* can face.
Each seal pup that's born to its mother
(And most mothers have only one)
Is commonly known as *a white-coat,*
Once its life at two weeks has begun;
And its fur that is long and so fluffy
Is its camouflage out in the snow,
Whilst it watches and waits for its mother,
As she leaves it to feed on the floe.

It has no fear whatever of hunters,
Since it's never seen humans before;
It just sees a new friend approaching,
With no thought of what is in store.

Two most beautiful eyes wide with wonder,
So shining and dark in the white;
A baby's eyes, trusting and hoping,
That will never again see the light.

If only our pups weren't so lovely,
Or so white, that one just holds one's breath;
But for this they are slaughtered in thousands,
And shot, or just bludgeoned to death.
It's an annual event in these regions,
Each pelt is another man's gain;
But good men still turn from the slaughter,
Appalled at our loss and our pain.

So spare us a thought when you see us,
As we lie on a beach wild and free,
Or we wriggle up, just to be friendly,
All shining and wet from the sea.
Let the plight of our young call for justice,
All you men that call here from far lands;
For with you we must look to the future,
And our future is all in your hands.

THE GREAT WHITE SHARK

I know you will have heard of me,
(I think most people would)
Although when I make headlines
the news is rarely good;
I only have two enemies
(and one of those is *Man)*
Who often goes to any lengths
to kill me if he can.

I'm like a great torpedo
as I rise from depths beneath;
I'm an awe-inspiring monster!
Just look at all my teeth!
I've roamed the Earth's great oceans
four hundred million years,
It's no wonder I strike terror
and I'm something mankind fears.

My only other enemy
that matches me in strength
Is the mighty killer whale,
of bigger, greater length;

I prey on whales and dolphins
whose names are known to you,
And otters, seals and turtles;
I prey on all those, too.

My mouth when it is open
is frighteningly wide,
Equipped with massive pointed teeth,
lined awesomely inside.
'Just like knives and forks' you'll say.
'What a fearsome sight!'
And so to man I say, 'Keep clear –
you'll not survive *my* bite!'

I hunt upon the tops of waves
as well as down below,
So even sea birds are not safe,
not many people know.
But as I'm so much hunted,
I'm endangered now, and so
In some lands I'm protected
I think the world should know.

I frighten and I fascinate;
I used to be half myth,
And those who see me hold their breath
and often look scared stiff.
But people (once they know me)
will respectfully remark,
*'There goes an ancient predator:
the mighty Great White Shark!'*

THE TREE SHREW

I look an unsuccessful cross
Between a squirrel and a rat;
And certainly I must admit
I look a bit like that.
In Malaysia you will find me,
But to find me it is true
You'll have to search for many hours
Without much of a clue.

You can hardly ever see me
Because I move so fast;
There's just a rustle of a leaf,
As I slip swiftly past.
My eyes like two glass buttons,
Will keep you on the trail,
But look for my long pointed nose,
And long, long bushy tail.

It's said that I'm related
To the family of Man;
And from small creatures such as me,
The primates all began.
I may be further down the line
Than scientists might think;
I might be on a different branch,
Or make a different link.

But one thing certainly is proved,
The point that's made is plain:
Compared to my small body size,
I have the biggest brain!

THE STRIPED SKUNK

I'm a pretty little mammal - and a clever one at that,
A cousin of the weasel and no bigger than a cat;
I live in North America - that's where I hope we meet;
You'll know me by my bushy tail, my snout, and short clawed feet.
I'm patterned with a long white stripe, but most of me is black;
There's a stripe upon my forehead and more right down my back.
And if upon my bushy tail you spy a flash of white,
You must admit you'd hardly find a more rewarding sight.
At night-time I am busy. That's when I hunt to eat;
I dig for worms and insects with the claws on my front feet.
But have you guessed my secret? Do you promise not to tell?
I've one impressive weapon: *a most disgusting smell!*
I use it to escape you know; it's not for every day;
But if there's someone chasing me - it makes them run away!

Of course I give fair warning. I stick my tail up straight,
I stamp my feet, I growl and hiss, and then I always wait.

My enemy might leave me then. I rather wish they would,
Just so I wouldn't have to spray - for everybody's good!
My smell is most atrocious; it can carry for a mile;
It hurts if it gets in your eyes, it really is most vile!
I'm the smelliest of mammals, a creature of renown,
And just the mention of my name will make most people frown.
But please don't let that put you off, if we should chance to meet:
Just see me as I *really* am - all cuddly, cute and sweet!

THE SLOTH

I'm not sluggish, I'm not lazy,
Just because I'm slow;
But I have to save my energy,
So that's the way I go.
Since *leaves* are mainly all I eat,
My food won't make me strong,
So I've got this reputation,
That is entirely wrong.

I like to do things upside-down,
As I'm sure you must have heard;
I eat, sleep, and give birth this way,
Which I know sounds quite absurd.
I hang from branches with my claws,
And swing there from my toes;
My hair hangs back to belly down,
You'd think that's how it grows.

Of course it's handy when it rains,
And when it rains - it *pours*,
But then the rain just runs straight off,
And only wets my paws.
I have a tail, but that's quite short,
In fact it's rather small,
So when I'm hanging from a tree,
You don't see that at all.

Two kinds of sloth have just *two* toes,
Three kinds of us have *three;*
You really have to look – and count,
To see which one is me.
And how surprised you'll be to learn
That all of us can swim.
You'll say, as I come sailing past,
'I can't believe that's him!'

My ancestor the Great Ground Sloth,
Who once lived long ago,
Was the same size as an elephant
You'll be amazed to know.
But *I* can't walk upon the ground,
If forced, I have to crawl;
My limbs cannot support my weight,
I've not much strength at all.

I'm the slowest moving creature
That lives on Earth today;
But scare me, and I'll move quite fast
If once I'm seen as prey!

You might not know I take *one month*
To digest just one meal;
Its things like this which sound so odd,
That gives me such appeal.

But come to South America,
And find me if you care;
You'll find me upside-down of course,
But I promise I'll be there.

THE SOLENODON

I'm the very proud possessor
Of a very special snout;
An extremely useful asset
For sniffing all about.
You'll see my snout a long, long time,
Before the rest of *me*;
It sort of bobs along the ground,
Or slips behind a tree.

I'm a kind of shrew-like creature
With an antiquated look;
But no matter where you search for me,
However hard you look,
I'm sure you'll never find me
In an ordinary book.
I'm a most endangered species,

Though a not unusual kind,
For my other close relations
Are much easier to find;
They're just moles, or shrews, or hedgehogs,
Not exciting you'll agree;
But where on earth could someone find
A creature quite like me?

There's just *two* islands in the world,
Both close to one another;
Hispaniola is the one,
And Cuba is the other.

If you look for me in daylight,
I expect I'll be asleep
In a burrow or a hollow tree;
And then you'll have to *peep*.
But if I'm frightened badly,
Then I'll really have to run;
And when you see my poor attempts,
You'll think I'm having fun.

I can't run straight – in one straight line!
I try and try in vain;
I 'zig-zag' or I 'waddle',
Then hang my head in shame.
And if I try to put on speed
And follow my long nose,
I tumble head-first-over-heels,
Or step on my own toes!

I have to warn you - when I'm cross
I frequently go mad;
I scream and bite without due cause,
My manners are quite bad.
And then if *that is* not enough
To give a nasty fright,
I must confess to one more thing -
I have a poisonous bite!

When I'm excited I might grunt
Or scream (as I have said),
But when I'm caught I'll stay quite still,
And simply hide my head.

So since I'm such an oddity,
I'm also rather rare;
And *soon (*tomorrow it might be)
I'll simply not be there!

THE EMPEROR
TAMARIN
MONKEY

If you spy a tiny monkey
In a forest in a tree,
The strangest one you've ever seen,
That monkey may be me.

My proper name is Tamarin,
But that's just *half* my name;
I'm also called an emperor,
From one who brought me fame.
It all began as just a joke
I'm led to understand,
Because of one important man
Who was so very grand.

He had a droopy long moustache
Of which he was so proud;
But soon when they discovered *me*,
The people laughed out loud:
'Oh, Wilhelm, look!' they shouted,
(For Wilhelm was his name)
*'A monkey with a long moustache -
A white one – just the same!'*

Apart from this moustache of mine,
I've black hands and black head;
My under-parts are white as snow,
My tail is orange-red.
You'll find me in the tropics
In places like Peru,
Where I feed on fruit and flowers,
And sip the honey dew.

I can climb just like a squirrel
To search for my small prey;
And ants, and snails, and tree bugs,
Are some that come my way.
I'll also sometimes catch a frog,
A lizard's tasty, too;
Or sometimes I might find an egg
That's fun to bite right through.

We Tamarins are very cute,
We're loved by every child;
And though we're often kept as pets,
We're threatened in the wild.

Our loss of habitat's to blame,
Our forest shrinks each day,
And oh, it's sad to think that we
Might vanish quite away.
I think the children love us most,
Because we look so posh;
Just like that German Emperor
With his grand long white moustache!

THE TAPIR

I've got the body of a pig,
(I'm *not* a pig of course),
I look more like an Anteater -
But I'm closer to a *horse*.

If the horse in prehistoric times
Had stayed where it should be,
In the jungle - where I am today,
It might have looked like *me*.
I'm related to the Rhino'
I think that you will find,
With four toes on my front feet,
And three on those behind.

A trunk is where my nose should be,
A kind of rubbery hose,
Much smaller than an elephant's,
But useful I suppose.
I use it when I sniff out food

To reach the leaves of trees;
I grab, then place them in my mouth,
And hope that I won't sneeze!

I trot and gallop like a horse,
(We're cousins I've heard tell)
But *I* can walk on river beds
And feed down there as well.
My swimming skills are excellent,
It's water I love best;
I'm either *in* or *under* it,
Except when I'm at rest.

You might just catch me lazing
If the sun is extra hot;
But don't think that I'm lazy;
That's one thing I am *not.*
You've got no chance of catching me
If *I* should choose to run;
There must be races everywhere
A tapir could have won.

I'm such a curious sight to see:
My front is coloured black,
The rest of me, a ghostly white,
Is saddled on my back.
That's why the moonlight suits me well,
With shadows round each tree;
So if a ghostly shape slips past
You'll never know it's *me!*

THE TARSIER

I'm one of several mammals
Like a lemur, monkey, man;
But on the scale of evolution
In the newly worked out plan,
It's the lemur and the monkey
That I am placed between;
Yet I'm still the smallest primate
I'm sure you will have seen.

One easy way to tell my size
And help you understand:
Just pick me up – and then you'll see
I'll fit inside your hand.
I look rather like a gremlin
I think you will agree;
Somewhat scary, yet quite cute,
But harmless - that is me.

I almost fly, I jump so high,
And have you seen my eyes?
They really are enormous,
And my ears are giant size.
My hands have little suction pads,
So I'll climb any wall;
I'll walk right up a pane of glass
And never ever fall!

Just like an owl I'll turn my head
Right round from back to front,

So I can watch all sides of me;
I use this trick to hunt.
I hunt at night – perhaps you've guessed,
And hide in every tree;
I'm like a gremlin, as I've said,
And quite a mystery.

My tail is very long indeed,
It seems to have no end;
I use it like an extra leg
And treat it like a friend.
My home is in the Philippines
And Indonesia, too;
I don't live long inside a cage,
I can't abide a *Zoo!*

I know I'm very loveable,
But leave me where I am;
I'll not be happy as a pet,
I'm happy as I am.
I'm one of Nature's little gems,
On the 'endangered list';
And if I go - as soon I might,
How sorely I'll be missed!

There's nothing left on earth you see,
That can compare with *me*;
I'm the cutest most unusual thing
That lives upon a tree.
But our numbers dwindle every day,
A sorry sight to see;

And with so many trees cut down,
There's less and less of me.

Here in my tree top house I stand,
The last left of the few;
But how long can I still remain?
The answer lies with *you*.

THE TASMANIAN DEVIL

I'll snarl and shriek, and screech, and scream,
To make your bones all shiver,
Enough to turn your blood to ice
And leave you all a-quiver.
My island home Tasmania,
From which I get my name,
Is now the place upon the map
Which gives me claim to fame.

I'm a devil who has come to Earth
To do what I must do:
Tease you and torment you -
And shake you through and through.

I'm coloured black, so in the dark
I'm difficult to see;
You'll find a shadow lurking there -
But look again: *it's me.*

I might be small and dog-like,
But I'm built just like a bear,
With teeth to match my appetite,
So I warn you – just beware!

I've horn-shaped fur upon my head,
Just like the devil's own;
And though you might say 'he looks cute',
I've got a heart of stone.
If my prey is dead or dying,
Whether big or whether small,
I'm a carnivorous marsupial,
And will eat them - bones and all!

My ears are coloured palest pink,
But watch if they turn *red*,
It's a sign that I am angry
And something you should dread.
Look also at my hairy tail,
It tells what state I'm in:
If it's *fat* – then I am healthy,
If I'm not - my tail is *thin*.

My fan club in Tasmania
All hope that I'll stay here;
But since I'm now in short supply,
I may well disappear.
They'll have to take good care of me
To keep me 'on the stage',
To see me lunge, and thrust, and pitch,
When I get in a rage.

The performance I will give you
Will be the best you've known;
Who else could thrill and still your heart,
And chill you to the bone?
I've the voice sound of a cyclone,
I'm a hellish kind of brute;
But you'll always hear my fans declare,
'Oh, don't you think he's cute?'

I'm a devil who has come to Earth
To do what I must do:
Tease you and torment you -
And shake you through and through!

THE THORNY DEVIL

I'm a Moloch from Australia,
So that *Moloch* is my name;
But listen - I will try to tell
Of how I came to fame:

A demon king lived long ago,
Of whom most people do not know,
Who smeared himself with human blood,
And Moloch was his name.
I'm not the monster people think,
Bloodthirsty; giant size;
In fact, if we should meet by chance,
You'd have one big surprise;
I'm just a lizard, after all,
A lizard that is rather small,
But very well disguised.

I'm camouflaged in desert shades,
In golden tan or brown;
I'll change to suit the temperature
As it goes up or down;
I'm darker when the weather's cold,
And paler in the sun, I'm told,
Which gives me great renown.
I look quite like a wind-blown leaf
Just trembling in the breeze;
One moment I will slowly move,
Next moment I will freeze;
I look quite like a dinosaur,
A baby one – that does not roar,
In fact I'm quite a tease.

The thorny spines that cover me,
Give me another name:
I look quite like a dragon,
So a dragon I became;
I'm called *a thorny devil,* too,
A name to scare you through and through,
That's how I came to fame.

A thorny devil I might be,
But guess what food I eat?
It's *ants* I'll stick my neck out for,
And they're my daily meat;
But birds give me an awful fright!
I keep my head well out of sight
If we should chance to meet!

I also own a secret head,
To foil my every foe;
It sits upon my spiny neck; it isn't *real* – as
real heads go;
I simply pop my real head *in*,
And leave outside its knobby twin,
So enemies won't know.

I don't drink in the normal way,
And here I'll give a clue;
I'll immerse myself in water,
That's one thing I can do.
And the way I take the water in?
I just absorb it through my skin!
It's very weird – but true.

My body with each groove and ridge,
Makes channels for the dew,
And when enough has gathered there,
It forms a pool or two;
Each pool will then begin to move
Towards my mouth from every groove,
So I can drink a few.

It's said that I'm endangered now,
And yet there is a plan
To use the formula *I* use,
Store water as *I* can.
Imagine now – what good advice
If someone used that same device
To help the cause of man!

THE BENGAL TIGER

Of all the forest I was lord,
Respected, feared, obeyed,
The roaring of my mighty voice
Made everything afraid.
Once I could lurk unseen, unknown,
I hardly knew a foe,
And with my strength I knew no fear;
But that was long ago.

From grassland with my camouflage
I watched to hunt for prey,
Where wild life bounded everywhere;
But that was yesterday.
Before my boundaries grew so small,
Before I'd heard of *men*,
Mine was all my eyes surveyed;
The world was different then.

The length and breadth of Asia,
In all terrain we'd go,
One hundred thousand of us all,
One hundred years ago.
But then those figures dwindled down
To deal a further blow,
There were thirty thousand of us left,
Just thirty years ago.
And now we totter on the edge,
Of hope almost bereft;
Of all that's wild that's left alive,
How many are there left?
Three species that have lately gone
Are now proclaimed extinct;
And are we soon to follow on?
Are all our futures linked?

I'm the largest most enchanting cat
The world still longs to see;
And though the lion springs to mind,
He's not as prized as *me*.
A pure bred tiger bold and big,
Can justly claim his fame;
His stripes are like man's fingerprints -
No two are quite the same.

Among the big cats only one -
The jaguar, I know,
Will dare to swim like me for miles,
And go where I will go.

For I will leap nine metres clear
In just one single bound,
Or climb a tree, lie sleeping there,
Then drop without a sound.

I'll not be found so easily,
My feet will leave no mark
Through grasses where I softly creep,
With eyes that pierce the dark.
I'll often bring wild cattle down
That weigh a ton or more,
And there's never a more deadly bite
Than from a tiger's jaw.

From India to Cape Comorin,
I hunt and make my home,
But I never travel with a pack;
A tiger hunts alone.
When hungry I'll take smaller prey,
A lizard if I wish,
Or frog, or fowl, or crocodile;
I'll even catch a *fish.*

If we should meet - don't turn and run,
But face me if you dare;
I'll glare at you with yellow eyes,
But show that you don't care.
Unless I'm hungry - if you shout
I might just turn away
And leave you gasping with relief
To live another day.

What power combined with so much grace
Can thrill the way *I* do?
The symbol of a continent,
Last of the glorious few.
No beast on earth's more beautiful
Than *a tiger* you'll agree;
And man should move both heaven and earth
To save the last of **me.**

THE ALDABRA GIANT TORTOISE

In the Western Indian Ocean
Are islands where I get my name;
If *Aldabra* you can't remember
Try that magic trick or game:
Abracadabra – that might help –
I think it sounds a bit the same.

Beyond the Seychelles plateau
You'll find my island home;
You'll know me by my massive size –
A giant shell shaped dome;
And grasslands, swamps, and coastal dunes
Are where I like to roam.

You won't believe what I can do –
You think I'm dull and slow?
Well, if you listen carefully,
There are things that you should know;
Like reaching up with my long neck -
A meter high I'll go.
My search for food can cause a stir,
I'll push; I'll heave and dig;
And if I see some juicy leaves

Above me on some twig,
I'll even cause a *tree* to fall.
I'm strong – as well as big.

My swimming skills are excellent,
Have you the faintest notion
How many cousins I have got
Who swim the Indian Ocean?
And all have my ability
To move with perfect motion.

I have a secret trick I do,
Not everybody knows;
When I have to drink from pools,
I bend my head towards my toes,
And, rather cleverly, I think,
I drink water through my *nose*.

An Aldabra giant tortoise
Can live two hundred years,
And yet there's something you should know -
A thing one rarely ever hears:
An accident quite small can be
The only thing a tortoise fears.

I must beware of falling off
High places where I climb;
Or tipping over, wrong side up,
For any length of time.
For to lose a creature such as *me*
Would surely be a crime!

THE TUATARA

I'm an actual living legend:
Tuatara is my name,
I'm a most amazing reptile of science fiction fame.
I may *look* like a lizard, but a lizard I am not,
I'm called a living fossil - a creature time forgot.

I'm very, very interesting,
but also very rare,
New Zealand is my only home;
you'll have to seek me there.
And to give at least a mention
of the measure of my worth,
I'm now evolving faster
than any creature found on Earth.

I'm a kind of living dinosaur
(the last one of my kind)
The most ancient group of reptiles
that time has left behind;

And if we're counting time in *years*,
as far as I can see,
Two hundred million is the score
recorded now for me.

I've tooth-like spines along my neck
and more along my back,
They make me look so big and bad
that others don't attack;
My enemies are mainly birds,
but since I hunt at night
For creatures of the insect kind –
I'm mostly out of sight.

Believe me, when I tell you
that I've also got *three* eyes,
And I'll hold my breath for *one hour long*;
another big surprise!
But I'm temperature dependent;
one more fact that makes me strange,
So now my life hangs by a thread
because of climate change.

The temperature must be just right
or quite soon I'm afraid
There'll be no female offspring
in the place my eggs are laid;
And consider my uniqueness –
I can live one hundred years,
I've survived ice ages, floods and earth-
quakes; all those kind of fears.

Isn't it just possible
one day I'll rule the Earth?
After all, I've been here
since the dinosaurs gave birth.
I know its wishful thinking
but it's still a valid query,
Since many people don't believe
the evolution theory.

Just imagine if I ruled the Earth
the same way man has done,
I could colonize the planet
and be Reptile Number One!
I think it might be feasible
the way that history goes;
If evolution's just a theory
It could well be. *Who knows?*

THE GREEN SEA TURTLE

I'm one of seven species,
A reptile who breathes air;
And if you travelled back in time,
You'd find me. I was there.
One hundred million years ago,
And over fifty more,
I first adventured out to sea,
And scrambled to the shore.

I swim the world's great oceans,
And in the long sea grass
I watch out for the larger sharks,
And other fish that pass.
Sometimes I travel many miles,
One thousand, maybe more,
Until I reach where I was hatched;
The same beloved shore.

It's awkward walking over land,
I often need a rest,
But there upon the sandy beach,
I dig and make my nest.
I'll lay about one hundred eggs,
Or maybe even more,
Then cover all of them with sand
And leave them on that shore.

The same night then, without delay,
I'll scurry to the sea,
As if they're no concern of mine;
No longer part of me.
But two months later - what surprise!
Imagine then the sight,
A hundred little turtle eggs
Hatch out at dead of night!

It's the moonlight on the water
That guides them with its glow;
No mother's helping hand for *them*
To show them where to go.
Only *one* in every thousand
Will survive to reach the sea,
As they scramble over sand dunes
In a mad dash to get free.

It's one wild fearful race for life,
For these poor desperate things;
There's danger in the crabs that crawl,
As well as birds with wings.

There's danger if they stay too long
To bake beneath the sun;
And in the sea the larger fish
Will eat them, every one.

A turtle with his flippers
Is quite clumsy on his feet,
And we wouldn't cover many miles
If you and I should meet.
In the ocean it's quite different,
Where I forage deep and wide;
I'm a fast and powerful swimmer,
If you wish to take a ride.

I eat a lot of sea foods
Too numerous to tell:
There's seaweed, jellyfish, and snails,
And shrimps and crabs as well.
I'm coloured green, and get my name
From seaweed that I eat;
The pastures near the shore I find
Are often quite a treat.

My natural life spans eighty years;
Great news you'd think for me;
But I've such a lot of predators
I meet when I'm at sea.
The worst one is the tiger shark,
Not to mention *man*;
They're always lurking somewhere near
To catch me if they can.

I'm supposed to be protected,
Which is good you must agree;
No person living on the land
Should kill or capture *me.*
For those who do not heed the law,
There's little I can do;
But at least, since now you know the score -
I hope it won't be ***you!***

THE LEATHER BACKED TURTLE

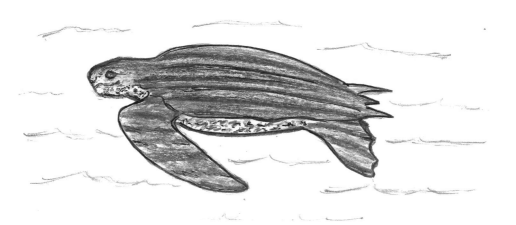

There's not a person living
who can estimate my worth,
I'm the largest reptilian animal
left upon this Earth;
The serpent found in legend
that lived beneath the sea,
Was a monster from a species
that was closely linked to me.

The distance and the depths I swim
will make you turn quite pale,
I'm the deepest diving reptile
diving deeper than a whale;
And if that takes your breath away,
I'll tell you one more thing:
I'm heavier than a polar bear;
I'm *twice* the weight of *him!*

A satellite has tracked my course –
the longest journey yet,
It is really so exciting
that a record has been set.
Halfway across the planet
is the journey that I took,
And I hope you read about it
in the Guinness Record Book.

You can really not imagine
all the sea miles I have crossed,
And of course you can be certain
that I'm never *ever* lost!
If you ask me how I do it
when I'm swimming out at sea,
I have a secret compass
that I carry round with me.

I suspect it works by instinct
with the sea; the sun; the light;
And all those things inherited
that give me 'second sight'.
No-one knows the answer
so everyone's in doubt;
The scientists don't understand;
they just can't make it out!

I cannot be confused of course
for any other kind
Of turtle living in the sea,
that you may one day find.

I'm the only turtle living
that hasn't got a shell;
When you see my leather patchwork,
that's the way to tell.

It takes me hours to dig my nest
once I set foot on land;
I lay about one hundred eggs
then cover them with sand;
But people harvest every egg
for greed that they can reach,
So soon I'll be unable
to nest on *any* beach!

We leather-backs love jelly fish –
and that is common news,
But *plastic* looks the same to us
and gives no obvious clues;
By the time that we ingest it,
in our eager happy haste,
We choke on what turns out to be
just floating deadly waste.

We've lived on Earth so long it seems
almost since time began,
One hundred million years they say,
from records kept by man;
But now we're marked 'endangered'
and it seems so very wrong
That in just another few short years
we could all of us be gone.

Some say I live one hundred years,
some people are unsure,
It's said that I may even live
about *two hundred* more;
But it's certain that I'm quite unique –
a monster from the sea,
Like the serpents in the legend
that were once a part of me.

THE WATER VOLE

Remember me? I'm 'Ratty'
From the book that gave me fame;
But I'm not a water rat at all,
So that is *not* my name.
To call a water vole 'a rat'
Is really such a shame,
And he who wrote that famous book
Must really take the blame.

I was the friend of mole, you see,
In *Kenneth Grahame's* book;
And 'mole' and 'vole' sound much the same,
So that was why he took
The liberty of changing names,
To state which one was which;
And I was given brown rat's name
In case there was a hitch.

You'll know me by my furry tail,
And little flat brown ears;
You'll spot the difference straight away
As soon as rat appears.
His ears are big and stick right out,
He's got a pointy face;
And *his* tail is pink and hairless,
A positive disgrace!

Such creatures as the tiger,
And the famous Panda bear,
Are *known* to be endangered,
So are given extra care;
But *I* speak for the humble vole,
And I must have my say:
*'I'm the most endangered mammal
In the British Isles today.'*

I only feed on water plants,
I don't do any harm;
And yet I'm disappearing fast,
And causing much alarm.
There's lots of things that can be done
To halt my sad decline,
To give me back a little part
Of wetlands that were mine.

I need fresh water where I live
To be pollution free,
(Brown rat doesn't mind some dirt,
He's not as clean as *me*.)

If I don't succumb to predators,
Like the heron, pike, or owl,
It's almost certain somewhere close
A mink is on the prowl!

So please, when next you're visiting
A marshland water hole,
Look hard to mark the difference;
Is it *rat* or *water vole?*
Please don't mistake me for a rat,
Because I look his size;
I'm chubby faced with rounded nose:
Just learn to use your eyes!

THE WALRUS

The walrus is a mammal
Of the highest high degree,
No seal that you can mention
Wherever he might be,
Can boast a set of tusks like mine
Which grow so splendidly.

It makes a walrus different
From all seals that you might meet;
And though I'm big and ugly,
And you couldn't call me *sweet,*
To see me ploughing through the waves
Will always be a treat.

I patrol the North Atlantic,
The North Pacific, too;

And following me close behind
Will be my trusty crew,
Who watch for drifting ice-bergs
To hitch a ride or two.

My two front teeth – those fearsome tusks,
Soon grow to massive size,
And these I use to cut through ice;
A needful exercise.
They also serve as weapons,
Which should be no surprise.

My diet is a varied one
Of catch within the sea:
There's shellfish; squid; there's crab or shrimp,
Or octopus, maybe.
I fish the shallows first, because
It's easier for me.

We walrus are intelligent,
We're one of the elite;
And that's because we socialise
With everyone we meet;
To hear a walrus symphony
Is certainly a treat.

We use our flippers, lips, and tongues,
As instruments for song;
The noise we make sounds rather like
A hammer or a gong;
And you can hear us *miles* away,
Our voices are so strong.

On land we're such big clumsy lumps,
We're helpless on the shore,
And we lie there in our thousands
Almost cheek to jaw;
So we're easy prey for hunters
Who kill us by the score.
They kill us for our massive tusks
For ivory, to sell,
And they strip us of our blubber
To use for oil as well;
It's been the same for centuries,
As far as I can tell.

So strong the bonds of friendship are,
That bind us to each-other,
We'll fight unto the very death
To try to save a brother;
It seems the instincts that we share
Are like those of a mother.

I've only three real predators,
When all is said and done:
The first must be the polar bear,
From whom all creatures run;
And secondly the killer whale,
Who's feared by everyone.

But lastly, and by far the worst,
My enemy is *Man,*
Who has killed for greed consistently,
Almost since time began.

It's ironic we must look to *him*
To bring about a ban!

But to all who love the walrus,
I have one last surprise;
Creep close and gently 'blow' at him,
And watch him close his eyes.
He'll bleat and grunt, and snort at you,
You'll have to heed his cries -
Because, you see, it's always been
His favourite exercise.

You'll almost hear his inner thoughts,
'Oh, do it please once more!'
And if you do - you'll know that he
Will love you evermore.

THE WARTHOG

Brains before beauty that's what people say,
And you can't blame a warthog for thinking this way.
Graceful or handsome is something he's *not,*
But just count the other good points that he's got:

'I'm clever,' *says he,* 'and though ugly, I'm strong,
I can run very fast for my legs are quite long;
I'm artful in lots of the things I can do,
I'm always adapting to threats that are new.
Endangered? *Not me!* I'm still wild and free,
And in African country you'll find lots of me.

'Leopards, lions and cheetahs, to name but a few,
Will always be dangerous whatever I do;
And though I will fight them, I try to refrain,
And employ other tactics – like using my brain.
If day-time proves risky (I much prefer light)
I'll turn things around and I'll forage at night;

And I won't die of thirst if no water is near,
I can live without *that* several months of the year.

'I've very long tusks and the warts on my face
Which make me look ugly and such a disgrace,
Are small plates of armour, protection from bites,
And the bumps and the buffets I get from my fights.
My body is hairless; I'm like everyone
Who has the same problem: I burn in the sun.
So I wallow in mud, that wonderful stuff,
Where I stay till I'm cooler. I can't get enough!

'A warthog goes charging all over the place,
And it's not that he's fiery or eager to race;
He will keep up his guard with young ones to tend,
For he always makes sure of a foe or a friend.
He sticks his tail *up* when he's running in fear,
With the tip hanging *down* to show danger is near;
But if he's out grazing with no foes around,
He might rest awhile and just kneel on the ground.

'*You* might feel quite lazy each day when you rise;
It might be an effort to open your eyes;
You might want to stay there to just clear your head,
As you stretch and you yawn - and you crawl from your bed.
But I tell you a warthog knows nothing of this,
He shares no luxurious moment of bliss;
For him there is hardly a moment to waste -
He must dash from his burrow in terrible haste.
For always outside is this horrible fear
That someone is lurking there ever so near;

So out he must rush in a quivering state,
For he's sure *someone - somewhere* - is hiding in wait!
He has to go out for he cannot stay in,
So the quicker he does it the better for him!

'But there's no substitute for a warthog like me,
A remarkable species that's still running free;
I've masses of courage; I'll fight if I must,
And then you won't see me for great clouds of dust!
But I'm only a pig, when all's said and done,
Although I admit *I'm the World's Number One.*'

THE BLUE WHALE

I'm not *a fish*, you realize that,
I'm a mammal, head to tail,
(And by far the most intelligent)
I'm the incredible Blue Whale.
All great oceans of the world
I look upon as home,
From the Arctic to Antarctica,
Where I often swim alone.

Through great grey seas I plough the waves,
Magnificent to see;
Nothing that lives or once has lived,
Compares with such as me;
Nothing of such enormous size
Has lived on earth before;
I make the mightiest beast seem small,
Even the dinosaur.

A glimpse will be enough to thrill,
But might cause some alarm,
And yet I'm gentle and quite shy
And don't mean any harm;
All I eat are tiny fish,
Those shrimp-like things called krill;
But *forty million* in one day,
I need to get *my* fill.

Watch me at my feeding time,
I'll make a dive and leap;
I'll do a headstand, wave my tail,
And plunge down really deep.
I can't breathe under water,
So I'll surface for some air,
And then I'll 'blow' both hard and high,
To give you quite a scare.

No animal has got my voice,
Of which I'm justly proud;
It makes one tremble just to hear
The songs I sing so loud.
My rumblings travel miles away,
Beneath the ocean waves;
Each call will then determine
The way a whale behaves.
It works just like a telephone
So whales can have their say,
And talk (like *you*) if they so choose
Hundreds of miles away.

If I should dare to come ashore
It's then I'd meet my fate;
Because I've got no heavy bones,
I'd be crushed by my own weight;
But supported by the water,
Since I'm always in the sea,
I've got no need for big strong bones,
To help to uphold *me.*

It's really quite incredible
The feats that I can do,
But there's one thing I find difficult -
I cannot *sleep* like you.
If I did, I'd quickly drown,
So I have to do my best
And take short naps and float a bit,
And that's the way I rest.

You may search the whole world over
For other whales at sea,
But there's none more gentle natured,
Or more likeable than me.
There were *three hundred thousand* of us once,
Before the whalers came,
But by the twentieth century,
They'd killed that much again.
We were almost all of us wiped out,
Almost on the brink
Of that final end of life on earth,
That tragic word *extinct.*

And though there's those who do their best,
Our future still looks grey;
There's about five thousand only
Of us left alive today.
Some populations I have heard,
Have had no hope *or* friend;
For them all help has come too late,
For them it is the end.
But what now of the rest of us?
Our future rests with *man;*
And our cry goes out to all of you,
Please save us if you can!

THE HAIRY NOSED WOMBAT

You won't see me in the daytime,
I'm very seldom out;
But those who come across me
Always stop, and point, and shout:
'Look! There goes a wombat
With his large and hairy nose!
I wonder where a wombat lives,
I wonder where he goes!'

So if you like, I'll tell you
The things that I can do,
If you meet me in Australia,
And I really hope you do.

I'm quite the rarest mammal
That burrows, left on earth,
With a pouch to keep my baby in,
A full six months from birth.

A wombat's pouch is back to front,
Which, though it sounds a sin,
Is specially made for burrowing,
So dirt cannot get in.

I dig deep holes and burrows,
That's the thing I do the best,
Then line a hole with sticks and leaves,
To make a comfy nest.
I sniff and snuffle as I dig,
In tunnels round about;
You cannot keep a wombat *in*,
Nor get a good one *out*.

I have a funny waddling walk,
Short legs and big strong paws;
But please be warned, a wombat has
Sharp teeth and also claws.
If I'm attacked I don't give in,
We wombats sure can fight!
Be careful of my four front teeth -
They give a fearsome bite!

You can't out-smart a wombat,
A wombat's brain is big,
And we know how best to use it,
We don't just blindly *dig!*
You can't out-run us either
(Just in case you thought you could)
We're strong as well as fast, you know,
You'd be trampled where you stood!

In fact I'm called 'a bulldozer'
I'm made of such strong stuff;
I've a rump that's like a toilet brush,
You can't bite it. *It's too tough.*

A wombat's clever (as I've said),
Please watch me eat my food;
I don't just grovel on the ground,
I think that's *very* rude!
Instead, just using one big paw,
(My front one if you please)
I put my food straight in my mouth,
And eat it all with ease.

In wild Australia where I live,
There's roots and grass to eat,
And since my teeth just grow and grow,
My life remains quite sweet;
And you really have no notion
How delightful life can be,
Just grazing in the grasslands,
For a wombat such as me.

I don't like being petted,
If I bite, you take the blame,
For a wombat's just a wombat,
And will always be the same.
But I'm hairy nosed and different
From the wombats you might meet;
I've longer ears and softer fur,
I'm somehow more *elite.*

And that's why I'm protected
(With my wombat friends, I mean),
For with the strains of modern life
We're few and far between.
So if you see me passing by,
Or working on my land,
Just wave, and pay your due respects.
I know you'll understand.

Wombat's closest relative is the Koala.

THE ZEBRA

Black stripes on white, white stripes on black,
That's all you can see from my front to my back;
A crossing's called after me as you might know,
That makes traffic stop so that people can go.

I look like a horse; we're related you see,
But *he's* not so strong or as sturdy as *me.*
I've excellent hearing, my vision is good,
And I'd never change places with *him* if I could!

I have to lie low when a lion's around,
So I nibble the grass and I don't make a sound;
He won't know I'm there, for I'm not easily seen
In the African sunlight with grass in-between.

But I run very fast when the going gets tough,
Till I hope that my enemy's had quite enough;
I can kick up my heels and vanish in dust,
And I'll do forty miles an hour, if I must.

Lions, leopards, hyenas, I most have to fear,
And I'll kick with my hooves if they dare to come near.
My home is the grasslands of Africa's plains,
Where there's plenty to eat if I follow the rains.

I'm noisy; I'm busy; and always alert
Watching out for the young ones in-case they get hurt;
When I whinny you'll think that there's been a mistake,
It sounds more like a *donkey* – the noise that I make.

I'll mingle with ostriches, antelopes, too,
When grazing it's something a zebra will do;
It's extra protection when danger's around
And means that I'm never so easily found.

Each of the patterns is different we wear,
If you look at our coats and you try to compare;
A mass of these stripes makes me harder to see,
And a lion might miss a small zebra like me.

Stripes help us stay in a tightly knit pack,
So we all look the same from the front to the back;
The *pattern's* important – not *colour* - and so
As the lion is colour-blind he doesn't know!

But our hope of survival is threatened I'm told,
From the loss of that territory we've known of old;
We're decreasing in numbers it's sad but so true;
How long will the zebra be living - like *you?*

THE ZORRO

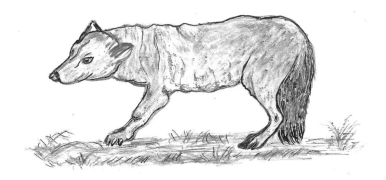

I'm not a wolf, and not a fox,
I'm something in-between;
Though you think I look familiar,
I'm not what I might seem.
In Spain I'm known as Zorro,
A most distinguished name;
And a zorro is the name for fox,
They really mean the same.

I'm long-haired and as bushy-tailed
As any fox you'll see;
But I'm not a fox, *or* dog, *or* wolf,
I'm a mixture of all *three*.
I've got webbed toes, would you believe,
On both of my hind feet,
By which I might be recognized
If ever we should meet.

There's very little known about
The short-eared type of me,
I live by swamps and river banks,
And swim efficiently;
I'll even catch a crab or two,
A lizard or a frog;
My many varied hunting skills
Will leave you all agog.

I'm the Zorro coloured *grey*,
Who's hunted for his coat;
It's no wonder that I'm hard to find,
My whereabouts remote;
It's also said I'm just a pest
For wildlife I might eat;
And it's true I'll catch a rabbit
Or a bird, just for a treat.

I also feed on rodents,
But I only eat my fill;
I often live on fruits alone,
But man still shoots to kill.
Yet one man once took up my name,
That hero of his age,
It was *Zorro the Adventurer*
Who took the centre stage.
And if you visit Argentina,
Or Chile, or Peru,
You might just catch a glimpse of me.
I really hope you do!